THE MARINE TURBINE

A historical review by a Swedish engineer

Part 2 1928 – 1980

The days of oil, steam and growth.
Development of naval turbines and the engines of the great Atlantic liners

by

Ingvar Jung

Maritime Monographs and Reports

No. 60 – 1986

Published by the Trustees of the National Maritime Museum

CONTENTS

List of tables

UNITS AND CONVERSION FACTORS

As there still is a great confusion in the use of metric and British Imperial units, conversion factors must be used for another generation before the SI–units are commonly accepted and established. Some important factors are listed below.

Units	British	Metric	SI
Length	1 ft	0.305 m	0.305 m
	1 in	25.4 mm	25.4 mm
	1 nautical mile	1.852 km	1.852 km
Weight	1 lb	0.454 kg	0.454 kg
	1 ton	1.016 tonne	1.016 tonne
Power	1 hp	1.014 hp_m	0.746 kW
	1.341 hp	1.36 hp_m	1 kW
	0.986 hp	1 hp_m	0.736 kW
Pressure	1 lb/in²	1/14.5 bar	1/14.5 bar
	1 lb/in²-gauge	(1/14.5 + 1 bar)	(1/14.5 + 1) bar
	14.5 lb/in²	1 bar	1 bar (10^5 N/m²)
Speed	1 knot	0.515 m/s	0.515 m/s
Consumption	1 lb/hph	0.448 kg/hp_mh	0.609 kg/kWh
	2.23 lb/hph	1 kg hp_mh	1.36 kg/kWh
	1.65 lb/hph	0.736 kg/hp_mh	1 kg/kWh

In most of the present data, the small differences between metric and British horse power, and between the metric ton and the British long ton have been disregarded as such accuracy would not be justified. Usually quantities are given by only two or three digits. There have also been difficulties in finding consistent data for steam pressures. Boiler pressures and pressures before the high pressure turbine are often mixed up. In general, the pressures given are boiler pressures. Throughout, British pressure units are given as 'gauge' values, metric and SI as 'absolute' values. For gears number of revolutions are noted for high and low pressure turbines and propellers at maximum power. Power figures given are in general maximum values.

FOREWORD
to
Parts 2 and 3

A monograph published to an historical subject is both a record and a comment on the events and people concerned. In the case of these last two sections of his Monograph on the history of the marine turbine, Professor Jung har given readers a clear and well illustrated statement of the story and an opportunity to admire the great technical achievements of marine turbine builders, including gas turbines of recent times.

Those concerned overcame very considerable research and design problems in new fields of metallurgy and gearing, as well as in the manufacture of boilers to generate the steam pressures required, whilst maintaining safe conditions of operation. In addition they had to build on a very large scale, to provide the power necessary to propel the greatly increased size of war and merchant ships of the day. A glance at the fascinating illustrations, such as the one of the bull wheel for the Soviet KRONSTADT, which helped procedure the required power of 56.620 kW for this super battle cruiser will indicate the scale of achievement.

However, the total involvement was much greater, because the designers and builders had to work under intense pressure, the pressure of competition generated by the need for their firm to be awarded the contract for building the turbines and by the need of the shipowner to have thies new vessel on time to beat his rivals. These might be competitors for profits on Transatlantic passenger routes or rival naval powers trying to win a race for domination. It was a world of rapid expansion in trade, in naval strength and in size and power of chips. The need was urgent and the response of the engineers magnificent. Their turbines bore the brunt of stern tests in commercial usage and in two world wars with considerable success.

The Museum and the reader are fortunate that Professor Jung, who played a leading role in many of the developments has dedicated so much of his energies and knowledge to recording this fascinating technical history with such clarity and appeal.

David Proctor
National Maritime Museum

PREFACE
to
Parts 2 and 3

Several years have passed since Part 1, dealing with marine turbine developments from Parsons' pioneering "Turbinia" until 1927, was published. The writing of the subsequent marine turbine progress has been delayed for reasons beyond the author's control. When the material for the review was completed, the editors found it expedient to split it into two parts, Part 2 dealing with naval turbines and the great Atlantic Liners, Part 3 with merchant marine turbines and the development of marine gas turbines.

The status of the steam turbine for naval service remained unchallenged through World War 2 and into the sixties. Also for the largest and fastest passenger ships the steam turbine was the supreme prime mover, until the airliners gradually took over the trans-oceanic passenger traffic after World War 2.

Several factors such as the fast growth in the size of power demands of cargo ships and the progressive fall in the price of fuel created the basis for a renaissance of the marine steam turbine in the merchant marine. This renaissance period started in USA before World War 2 through the contracting of a great number of steam turbine-driven ships by U.S. Maritime Commission and lasted 30 years until the OPEC crises of 1973 triggered the abrupt end of the shipping boom.

During the eighties it has become increasingly apparent that the era of steam propulsion machinery at sea is at an end for both naval and merchant ships. The marine gas turbine, with its low weight and great flexibility is far better adapted for the naval ships of today than the more complicated steam plant. For merchant ships the low fuel consumption of the modern turbo-charged diesel engine makes it "Hors Concours" with the high fuel cost of the eighties. The only exceptions for steam drive are the nuclear submarines, cruisers and aircraft carriers, and possibly a few coal-fired ore and coal carriers.

It is therefore with a certain sadness that the author has tried to summarize the developments during the more than half-century he has been privileged to be active in the Age of Steam, which now seems to have passed into history without hope of return. Turbine builders, however, can find some consolation in that the science of turbine building is surviving in the new extremely sophisticated marine gas turbines, in the aircraft-type jet engines and also in the supercharging turbo-type units of the diesels. Without supercharging, diesel power could never have attained the position it holds to day.

Modern marine diesel engines have exhaust gas turbine-driven superchargers with compressor and turbine powers up to and over one third of the useful power.

Probably few engineers have been granted the privilege of living through such exciting developments as the author and his colleagues. Contact with experts in shipping companies, with naval architects and engine designers throughout the world, has resulted in bonds of friendship that have endured far into retirement.

The large amount of Swedish material in this history is perhaps understandable against the background of the authors's activities in the Swedish Navy and the Swedish turbine industry.

I hand this book now to its readers and at the same time thank all those who have helped me to write it.

Roy Lewis has worked hard to produce an accurate translation from the Swedish manuscript which has subsequently been amended in essential details by those named below. The Swedish illustrators, Nikolai Kowarsky and Bengt Kreuger, have contributed many of the drawings that add much to the written word. Mrs Git Sundt has with great care and skill produced the typescript.

My thanks go firstly to my old colleagues and to the British National Maritime Museum and its Trustees, as well as to the Institute of Marine Engineers of London, who have made the printing possible, and to all good friends who have checked and corrected the manuscript. A special acknowledgement to the Museum's Head of Printed Books Department, Mr David Proctor, for all his help and encouragement.

I owe a great dept of gratitude to Admiral Sir George Raper, Royal Navy, Mr Ronald Boddie, Institute of Marine Engineers, as well as to Mr Harold Semar, Westinghouse, and Mr Tom Steele, General Electric, USA. Dr Simon Archer has helped me in so great an extent that I hardly know how to thank him. Without him, the English versions of my book might not have seen the light of day. I am very obliged to GEC Turbine Generators Ltd of Rugby, G.B., General Electric's Marine Department, Lynn, to Mr J. Yamashita of Mitsui Heavy Industries, Mr Y. Sasaki of Sumitomo Heavy Industries, Japan, as well as to Kamyr Inc. of USA for their generous contributions to cover printing and binding costs.

Nacka, Sweden
July 1986

1. TECHNICAL INTRODUCTION

Kind and helpful colleagues and friends who read the manuscript found it somewhat difficult to understand for those not familiar with turbines. Following their advice, I have tried to give a short technical introduction to amplify the historical resumé given in Part 1, Chapter 1.

In steam turbine technology two different, yet parallel, systems have developed for transferring the energy in the boiler steam to the blades on the turbine rotor. The level of energy in the turbine inlet steam is higher than that in the turbine exhaust steam, which is then led from the turbine to be condensed in the seawater-cooled condenser. This heat drop is utilized and transferred to the moving blades in the turbine rotor with an efficiency that can be good or poor depending on the design. The higher the pressure and temperature of the steam at the inlet to the turbine, the greater is the heat drop that can be utilized. Both Parsons and his contemporary inventor of the steam turbine, de Laval, found that the blade velocity in a turbine stage, consisting of a row of stationary guide vanes followed by a wheel with moving blades, must be of a certain magnitude relative to the heat drop in the stage to achieve an acceptable efficiency of energy transfer to the moving blades.

Impulse turbines

In the impulse turbine, where the entire heat and pressure drop occurs in the stationary guide vanes, de Laval found that maximum efficiency occurred when the blade speed was about half of the theoretical speed that the steam would have attained if it had expanded without losses in the guide vanes. Thus the blade velocity should corrrespond to about half the velocity represented by the heat drop in the stage.

De Laval's single stage impulse turbine was therefore designed as shown in the diagram, fig. 1. The steam flow direction was changed in the moving blades without any drop in pressure and the greater part of the impulse from the steam was transferred to the blades. In the multi-stage impulse turbine, the steam expanded in a number of such stages, each consisting of stationary guide vanes and moving blades fastened to discs. As there was no pressure drop in the moving blades, they had no need of sealing against the turbine casing. On the other hand, the diaphragms supporting the guide vanes required sealing against the rotor. This was done with labyrinth glands, consisting of a number of knife-edged fins with a small radial clearance on the rotorshaft.

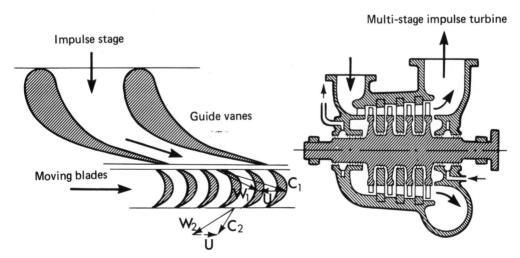

Fig. 1. Arrangement of a de Laval single impulse stage, and a multi-stage impulse turbine.

Reaction turbines

In the Parsons' reaction turbine, fig. 2, the heat drop in a stage is equally divided between the guide vanes and the moving blades. Parsons found that the moving blades in such a reaction stage needed a considerably higher peripheral speed to achieve maximum efficiency with the same heat drop as an equivalent impulse stage. The best efficiency was obtained at a blade velocity corresponding to about 70% of the steam velocity equivalent of the total stage heat drop. For the same blade velocity, the reaction stage could not use as great a heat drop. As the heat drop to attain a given velocity by expansion of the steam is proportional to the square of that velocity, it can easily be seen that for equal heat drops and equal blade velocities, the impulse turbine needs only half as many blade stages as the reaction turbine.

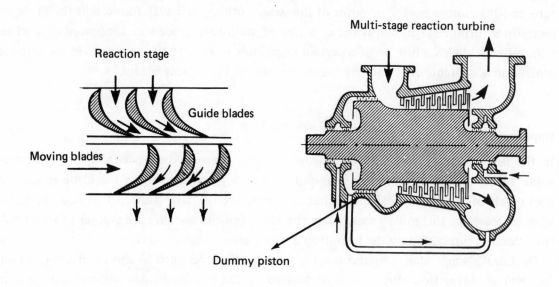

Fig. 2. Arrangement of a reaction stage consisting of identical guide and moving blades, and a multi-stage reaction turbine with dummy piston.

The rotor of an early reaction turbine was constructed like a drum in which the moving blades were fastened in circumferential grooves. The guide blades were fastened in the casing in similar turned grooves. In contrast to the impulse turbine, there was a considerable pressure drop in the moving blades. This pressure drop resulted in an axial steam thrust upon the rotor in the direction of steam flow. To counteract this, Parsons used a sealed balancing device known as a dummy piston at the inlet end of the drum. The space behind the dummy piston was connected by a pipe to the steam exhaust. By such means, the axial thrust was balanced out. To locate the axial position of the rotor, both turbine designs used thrust bearings.

The Curtis double impulse stage

The double impulse stage was developed by the American inventor Curtis in 1895, and is shown diagrammatically in fig. 3.

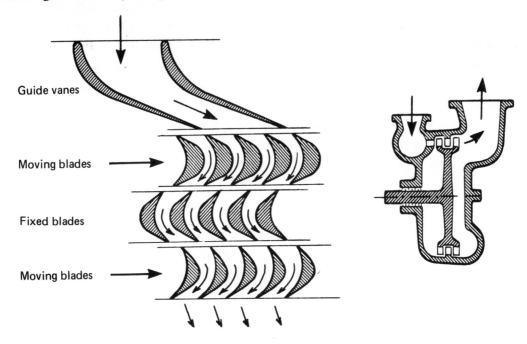

Fig. 3. Diagram of a Curtis double impulse stage with fixed guide blades between the two rows of moving blades.

The Curtis wheel offered a great advantage compared with one or even two single stage impulse wheels. In the Curtis wheel the whole heat drop in steam flow occurs in the guide vanes. In the second fixed blade row only the direction of the steam flow is changed, not the velocity. Therefore the Curtis stage can utilize twice the heat drop in the steam compared with two single impulse stages in series and four times the heat drop of one stage — theoretically the efficiency should be the same, but in reality the losses are somewhat greater. Two Curtis wheels in series in an astern turbine can therefore give about the same power as four single impulse or eight reaction stages.

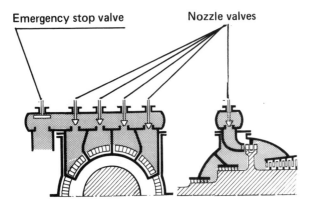

Fig. 4. Diagram of Curtis wheel with nozzle control governing and four nozzle groups.

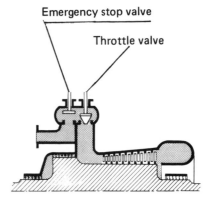

Fig. 5. Simple throttle governing of a reaction turbine.

The Curtis stage soon became used as a governing stage with partial admission, (i.e. nozzles extending over only a part of the circumference) for both impulse and reaction turbines. Considerable advantages were obtained at partial loads by dividing up the admission nozzles into groups, which could be opened to steam by separate valves as shown by fig. 4.

The turbine could thereby use full steam pressure at lower loads without the losses caused by throttling the steam. Considerable gains were thus made in comparison with the simple throttle governing shown in fig. 5. With throttle governing, the steam pressure before the first row of stationary blades varies linearly with the load. Thus if only quarter load is required, the steam pressure before the first row of blades will be only one quarter of the full steam pressure before the governing valve. With partial admission governing, the full steam pressure can be maintained at the nozzle valves of the Curtis stage without throttling losses in the nozzle groups, those required being fully open.

Gearing

De Laval realized from the beginning that his high speed impulse turbine needed gearing to be able to use the blade velocities that were necessary and have an acceptable output speed. Parsons, on the other hand, solved his problem initially by using a large number of blading stages with moderate speeds, thereby dividing the total heat drop up into many smaller steps. When operation at low rotational speeds was necessary, for example for propeller propulsion, Parsons too eventually found gearing indispensable.

Fig. 6 shows a single-casing impulse turbine with shrunk-on discs and single reduction gear of a classic design. The turbine had a governing stage of the Curtis type (5) with cam-operated nozzle valves (3) which controlled the steam to a number of partial admission nozzle groups (4). After the Curtis wheel followed seven turbine discs (7) fastened to the

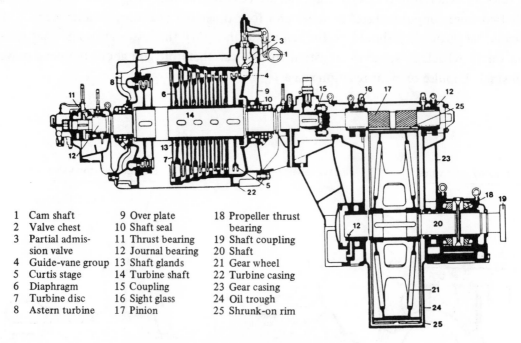

1 Cam shaft	9 Over plate	18 Propeller thrust
2 Valve chest	10 Shaft seal	bearing
3 Partial admis-	11 Thrust bearing	19 Shaft coupling
sion valve	12 Journal bearing	20 Shaft
4 Guide-vane group	13 Shaft glands	21 Gear wheel
5 Curtis stage	14 Turbine shaft	22 Turbine casing
6 Diaphragm	15 Coupling	23 Gear casing
7 Turbine disc	16 Sight glass	24 Oil trough
8 Astern turbine	17 Pinion	25 Shrunk-on rim

Fig. 6. Section through a small geared marine impulse type
turbine for a mine-sweeper from the thirties.

turbine shaft with a shrink fit and keys. The diaphragms (6) carrying the guide vanes were located in grooves in the turbine casing (22) and had labyrinth glands (13) sealing against the shaft. The astern turbine (8) consisted of a Curtis stage and a single impulse stage. This arrangement, with full steam flow, gave an astern power of approximately half the ahead power, and proved sufficient for almost all types of vessels. The turbine shaft (14) was coupled to the gear pinion (17) by a flexible coupling (15). The double helical pinion was supported by bearings in the gear casing (23) and meshed with the main gear wheel (21) which consisted of a robust cast steel centre portion with a shrunk-on gear rim (25). The gear wheel was fastened to the thrust shaft (20) by a shrink-fit and keys. The thrust bearing (18) counteracted the axial thrust from the propeller. All bearings and teeth were lubricated by oil under pressure from a separately-driven pump.

Reaction turbines and blade sealings

With Parsons' reaction turbine, effective sealing of both the fixed and moving blade rows was necessary. Parsons solved this problem with riveted-on shroud bands made from punched strip in segments covering from 6 to 12 blades in both fixed and moving rows. This shrouding had a thin-tipped axially protruding edge which sealed the fixed blade against the moving blade root, and the moving blade against the fixed blade root, fig. 7 A. As in the impulse turbine, the shrouding provided a strong support for the blades and hindered vibrations.

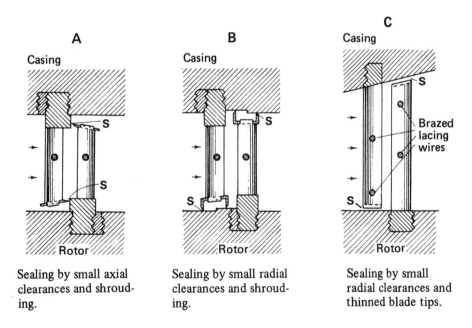

Sealing by small axial clearances and shrouding.

Sealing by small radial clearances and shrouding.

Sealing by small radial clearances and thinned blade tips.

Fig. 7. Various sealing methods for reaction blading.

Longer blades were strengthened by lacing wires threaded through holes in the blades and brazed to them. This "end-tightened" method of sealing, shown in fig. 7 A, was used for many years by Parsons Marine Company. The design, however, required the axial clearances to be kept very small, and this was done by fitting axially adjustable thrust bearings. A more effective way of sealing with radial clearances and double sealing fins, shown in 'B', was later developed by builders of stationary turbines. Several turbine builders on the Continent even developed radial seals where neither the fixed nor moving blading had shrouding, as shown in fig. 7 C. The blades were supported instead by lacing wires which ran through holes in the blades. The wires were fitted in sections and brazed so that a strong blade 'package' was achieved. By turning and fitting, the radial clearances were kept to a minimum. Both fixed and moving blades had their tips reduced to thin edges against the casing or shaft respectively. If the moving parts made contact during operation, the knife-edges were quickly worn down without causing damage.

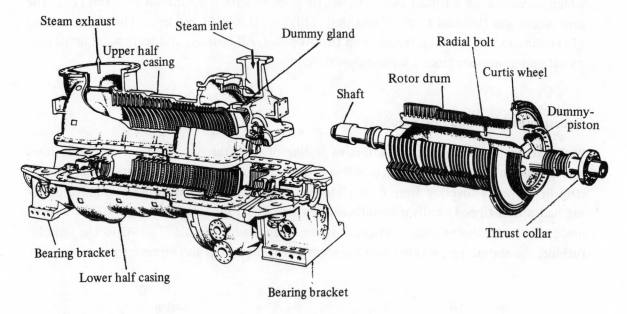

Fig. 8. Perspective drawing of the casing and rotor of a Parsons high pressure turbine from the 30's with a Curtis governing stage, rotor and reaction blading.

The design of a high pressure Parsons turbine from the 30's is shown in fig. 8.

The left-hand part of the drawing shows the turbine casing with the upper half lifted and the bearing brackets attached. The guide blades are fitted in grooves turned in the turbine casing, and are distributed around the entire periphery, except for the fixed blades and nozzles of the governing stage which only cover a part of the circumference. The right-hand part of the drawing shows the removed rotor with its Curtis governing stage, dummy piston and thrust bearing collar. The rotor is built up as a forged drum with the shaft end fastened to it by a shrink fit and radial bolts. The moving blades are fastened in grooves turned in the drum and governing stage disc.

2. TURBINE DEVELOPMENT IN THE U.S. NAVY

2.1 Inter-war period and the Second World War

When peace came after the First World War, the U.S. Navy found itself in possession of the largest navy in the world, and an enormous productive capacity in the shipyards and at the engine builders. All the larger types of ships were propelled by steam turbines. Broadly speaking, two-thirds of these turbines had been manufactured by the shipyards in their own engine works, and one third by the large manufacturers of land-based turbines, General Electric and Westinghouse. The considerable marine gear manufacturing facilities at the de Laval Company in Trenton, New Jersey, had also been fully utilized, but that company's turbine designs had not at this period received approval from the Bureau of Engineering. New large special factories had been built from the ground to satisfy the Navy's tremendous war-time demand.

Reaction and impulse turbines were fairly evenly divided in the U.S. Navy. The turbo-electric machinery in battleships had been shared by General Electric (impulse turbines) and Westinghouse (reaction turbines) and installed by both Federal and commercially-owned shipyards. The engine works at these yards had built turbines for destroyers under both Curtis and Parsons licences. General Electric and Westinghouse had succeeded in getting orders for about one-third of the propulsion machinery of the new-construction for the destroyer fleet. This consisted of two hundred and fifty practically identical flush-decked units of between 1100 and 1200 tons. They had standardized machinery of twice 8800 to 10000 kW (24000 to 27000 shp). Steam pressure was 19 to 20 bar (260 to 275 lb/in^2) for all of them, and not a single one had superheating.

Most of the units had geared, cross-compound turbines, where steam passes first a high pressure and then a low pressure turbine, each turbine rotor being coupled to a gear pinion. Some of the vessels had declutchable turbines in various arrangements.

The practically newly-built U.S. Fleet had from an international point of view, however, a rather one-sided make-up. Thirteen large turbo-electric battleships had been built since the outbreak of war, and four units of the 'Maryland' class were completed between 1921 and 1923. Six giant battlecruisers of 33000 tons with turbo-electric machinery of 4×33600 kW (180000 shp) were also on order, although four of them were cancelled before their keels were laid.

Experience during the war had shown a great need for light or medium cruisers with a long range of action. There had been no cruisers built since the three experimental ships of the 'Chester' class in 1903. Ten light cruisers of the 'Omaha' class were completed during the final stages of the war, it is true. They were powered by 4×16600 kW (90000 shp) geared cross-compound turbines, and had declutchable cruising turbines on two of the shafts, but this addition was considered quite inadequate by the naval strategists.

Thus it was that in 1918 the United States was internationally the leading nation as far as the number of warships was concerned. But the new-building activities were drastically reduced. The other Great Powers, Great Britain, Japan and France, showed on the contrary clear signs of starting a new arms race to catch up with the U.S. lead. A meeting was therefore called in Washington on the initiative of American statesmen to try to set a limit to the magnitude of naval armaments. The Washington treaty of 1921 contained, in principle, the following clauses:

1. Relative strengths of the five signatories were to be maintained in the tonnage proportion of 10/32 each for USA and Great Britain, 6/32 for Japan, 3/32 each for France and Italy.

2. The displacement of battleships and battlecruisers was to be limited to 35000 standard tons, and their main armament was not to have a greater calibre than 16 inches (40.6 cm). Total combined tonnage for USA and Great Britain was limited to 525000 tons. This meant that the USA could not complete the large battlecruisers 'Lexington' and 'Saratoga' already under construction.

3. Aircraft carriers were not to exceed 27000 tons. The United States, by means of an escape clause, managed to save the battlecruisers 'Lexington' and 'Saratoga' by reconstructing them as aircraft carriers, although they were of 33000 tons.

4. The displacement of cruisers was limited to 10000 tons, and their calibre limited to 8 inches (20.3 cm):

The primary need of the United States was for cruisers. The Washington cruisers 'Pensacola' and 'Salt Lake City' were approved in 1924 and made their trials in 1927. Their machinery has been described in Part 1. They were soon followed by the 'Northampton' class cruisers, all with yard-built Parsons turbines of $4 \times 20\,000$ kW (107000 shp). They were identical in power to the previous Washington cruisers, and were likewise fitted with declutchable cruising turbines connected to the HP turbines, see Table 1. These vessels were commissioned during 1930 to 1931.

In 1929, two more, somewhat heavier, Washington treaty cruisers of the 'Portland' class, and seven 'New Orleans' class were approved. Modernised boilers were introduced in the latter ships with an elevated steam pressure of 28 bar (390 lb/in^2). For the first time in U.S. cruisers, superheating was introduced. This resulted in a considerably better fuel economy and increased range of action.

However, it was in destroyer machinery that the greatest progress was to be made in the U.S. Fleet. After the mass production of destroyers during the First World War, there was a five year pause in building these greyhounds of the sea. Not until 1932 were appropriations for a new series of the eight destroyers of the 'Farragut' class approved, see Table 2.

Displacements were increased to 1400 tons, and the engine power was raised by more than one half. The steam pressure advanced to 29 bar (400 lb/in^2) and superheating to 340° (650°F) was introduced in connection with the new boiler designs. Higher steam conditions always bring some complications. To avoid corrosion and scale formation, the boiler water had to be kept clean with a very low concentration of salts, and also relatively free from oxygen. These factors brought demands for a more sophisticated feed water system. In the semi-closed system introduced at the beginning of the thirties a certain amount of deaeration took place in the condenser, thereby reducing boiler corrosion. Improved evaporators for producing cleaner condensate from seawater were also developed.

The boilers, however, were placed as before in a sealed boiler room, i.e. the forced draught fans pumped the combustion air directly into the pressurised boiler room. The boilers had steam generating tubes and superheater tubes, but no economisers, however. The exhaust gas temperatures were therefore high and boiler efficiencies low. No cruising turbines were installed. The declutchable cruising turbines had earned themselves a solid reputation for unreliability during the war, so much so that they were banished from the U.S. Fleet for ever. The 'Farragut' class turbines were build by commercial and Federal yards

Table 1.

Development of cruiser machinery in the U.S. Navy.
Inter-war period and the Second World War.

Launch year Deliv. year	Class Tonnage	No.	Power/1000 kW	shp	Speed knots	No. of shafts	Mach. arr.	Steam cond. bar/°C lb/in²/°F
1926–27 1929–30	Pensacola 9100	2	80	107	32,5	4	G[(HP+GCR)+LP] Pa	22 sat 300/sat
1928 1930–31	Northampton 9000	6	80	107	32,5	4	G[(HP+GCR)+LP] Pa	22/sat 300/sat
1931–32 1932–33	Portland 9900	2	80	107	32,5	4	G[(HP+GCR)+LP] Pa	22/sat 300/sat
1933–36 1934–37	New Orleans 9950	7	80	107	32,5	4	G(HP+LP) W	26/275° 375/525°
1936–38 1938–39	Brooklyn Wichita 9600/10600	10	75	100	32,5	4	G[(HP+GCR)+LP] Pa	28/360° 400/675°
1941–46 1942–46	Atlanta 6720	11	56	75	32,5	2	GG[(HP+CR)+LP] W	42/455° 600/850°
1941–43 1942–46	Cleveland 11740	41	75	100	32,5	4	GG[(HP+GCR)+LP] GE	42/455° 600/850°
1942–51 1944–53	Baltimore Worcester 14700	20	90	120	33	4	GG[(HP+GCR)+LP] GE	42/455° 600/850°
1943 1944	Alaska 29800	2	112	150	33	4	GG[(HP+GCR)+LP] GE	42/455° 600/850°
1946–47 1948–49	Des Moines 17260	3	90	120	33	4	GG[(HP+GCR)+LP] GE	42/455° 600/850°

Pa = Parsons
W = Westinghouse
GE = General Electric
sat = saturated steam

G[(HP+GCR)+LP] = single reduction, cross-compound turbine, with geared cruising turbine coupled to HP turbine.

GG(HP+ LP) = cross-compound turbine with locked-train, double reduction gear

under a Parsons licence. They were comparable to corresponding ships' machinery of the other Great Powers of that period.

Already at the beginning of the thirties, Franklin Roosevelt saw the storm clouds piling up on the political horizon as unemployment and crises in American industry got worse at the same time. After his inauguration as President in 1933, he attempted to break the Depression with his New Deal. He procured work for the shipyards by large orders for naval shipping. In that way he could build up a strong navy for future needs against aggression from dictators such as Mussolini and Hitler, and, not least, from the ever more apparent threat of the expanding Japanese Empire.

With Roosevelt and his great interest in the Navy, the U.S. Fleet entered a new era. Influence from Big Business was reduced, new designs were tried and things were no longer done in the old conservative way. That all this could not occur without birth pains and difficulties has been testified with feeling by Admiral Harold Bowen in his book 'Ship Machinery and Mossbacks'.*

* Princeton University Press, 1954.

Table 2.

Development of destroyer machinery in the U.S. Navy.
Inter-war period and the Second World War.

Launch year Deliv. year	Class Tonnage	No.	Power/1000 kW	shp	Speed knots	No. of shafts	Mach. arr.	Steam cond. bar/°C lb/in²/°F
1915–19 1916–20	WWI 1100	200	15/20	20/27	35	2	G(HP+LP) G[(HP+CR)+LP] Pa, Cu, GE, W	19/sat 260/sat
1934–35 1935–36	Farragut 1395	8	32	42,8	36,5	2	G(HP+LP) Pa	29/340° 400/675°
1935–36 1936–37	Mahan 1450	18	32	42,8	36,5	2	GG[(HP+GCR)+LP] GE	29/360° 400/675°
1935–36 1936–37	Porter 1850	8	37,4	50	37	2	G(HP+LP) Pa	29/360° 600/675°
1936–38 1938–39	Gidley 1600	4	37,4	50	38,5	2	G(HP+LP) Pa	42/370° 600/700°
1936–37 1938–39	Bagley 1650	8	36,5	49	38	2	GG[(HP+GCR) LP] GE	42/370° 600/700°
1937–38 1938–39	Somers 2050	5	38,8	52	37	2	GG[(HP+GCR)+LP] GE	42/370° 600/700°
1938–39 1939–40	Benham 1660	10	37,4	50	38,5	2	GG[(HP+GCR)+LP] GE W	42/370° 600/700°
1939 1939–40	Sims 1760	12	37,4	50	35	2	GG[(HP+GCR)+LP] GE W	42/370° 600/700°
1939–43 1942–45	Benson 1870	42	37,4	50	35	2	G(GHP+LP) Pa	42/455° 600/850°
1939–43 1942–45	Gleaves 1870	71	37,4	50	35	2	GG[(HP+GCR)+LP)] W GE	42/455° 600/850°
1942–44 1942–45	Fletcher 2375	181	45	60	38	2	GG[(HP+GCR)+LP)] GE W	42/455° 600/850°
1943–46 1943–46	Summer 2610	160	45	60	37,5	2	GG[(HP+GCR)+LP)] GE W	42/455° 600/850°

Pa = Parsons
W = Westinghouse
GE = General Electric
Cu = Curtis
sat = saturated steam

G(HP+LP) = single reduction, cross-compound turbine.

G(GHP+LP) = cross-compound turbine with double reduction HP turbine and single reduction LP turbine.

GG[(HP+GCR)+LP] = double reduction, locked-train, cross-compound turbine with geared cruising turbine coupled to HP turbine.

During 1933, no less than 18 destroyers of the 'Mahan' class were ordered. This large appropriation was justified by Roosevelt by the need to get industry moving and break the depression. With the placing of the orders, a radical change was made. Instead of requesting tenders, planning, from the big yards, the Navy commissioned the internationally renowned firm of consultants, Gibbs and Cox, to draft the destroyer project and prescribe detailed specifications which were to be the basis of the yards' tenders. This was to apply not only to the hull, but also to the machinery design and armament. Calculations and specifications were worked out in close collaboration with the yards and the large turbine and boiler specialists.

For the creation of the 'Mahan' class, the Bureau of Engineering thus gave Gibbs & Co a free hand to depart from the traditional turbine and boiler designs. Gibbs & Cox's foremost technologist, Gilliam Gibbs (1886 to 1967), had wide experience from project work with the building of land-based power stations and large merchant ships.

For steam power stations on land, steam pressures up to 64 bar (910 lb/in^2) and temperatures up to 455°C (850°F) had begun to be used. Feed water heating in several stages and superheat control had given exceptional improvements in both availability and fuel economy. General Electric had early realized the great saving to be attained by using small turbine rotors at very high speeds. Higher efficiencies were achieved, and because of the reduced masses of the turbine rotors and casings these were less sensitive to rapid temperature changes during manoeuvring. The high speeds, however, were only possible with double reduction gearing.

That William Gibbs dared to specify double reduction gearing together with small impulse-type turbine rotors, had its background in the advances made with developments at de Laval and General Electric. The U.S. Navy had given these two companies in 1932 a development assignment to design a reliable gear unit for large reduction ratios. This was to transform a turbine speed of 5000 to 6000 revs/min to a propeller speed of the order of 300 to 400 revs/min. The power requirement for the 'Mahan' class ships was 16000 kW (21000 shp) per shaft. The gears were to be dimensioned with margins of such magnitude that powers of 19000 kW (26000 shp) could be transmitted without risking reliability. In a surprisingly short time the joint development committee of the two companies, led by Richard Waller, chief engineer of the De Laval Company at Trenton, brought out designs for a double reduction, locked-train gear* for cross-compound turbines. Gear-cutting techniques were improved by development of more accurate hobbing machines by General Electric and Westinghouse, de Laval and Falk, as well as shaping machines by Farrel Birmingham, and new inspection instruments. By these means, the peripheral speeds in the gear mesh could be considerably increased, and the tooth loadings raised, resulting in smaller, lighter and more reliable gears.

This locked-train design subsequently became the dominant gear type for high outputs and high turbine speeds. William Gibbs and the Bureau of Engineering thus gave General Electric an order for completely new designs for the 'Mahan' class turbine units. The design principles introduced by the General Electric meant a very large step forward when compared with previous destroyer machinery, which is clearly apparent from Table 3.

The 'Mahan' turbine machinery was designed by the General Electric Co for a steam temperature of 455°C (850°F), for those days a normal temperature for new land-based power stations. The opportunity to improve the fuel economy of the 'Mahan' class, however, was never used, as the boiler manufactures did not dare to go to such a high superheat for fear of the thermal shocks during rapid load changes and manoeuvring. The boiler designs that were used had no control over the exit temperature from the superheaters. In the 'Somers' class, ordered in 1935, a start was made with temperature control by providing the boilers with two furnaces, separated by a tube bank. Flue gases from only one of the furnaces

---

*Locked-train gear = a double reduction gear, where the torque from the first reduction pinions is split between two wheels driving the two pinions of the second reduction. See text and fig. 22, page 32.

Table 3.

Comparison of turbine machinery for the 'Farragut', 'Mahan' and 'Somers' class destroyers.

Class Approv. year		Farragut 1932	Mahan 1933	Somers 1935
Steam data	bar/°C	29/350°C	29/360°C	42/370°C
	lb/in²/°F	400/650°F	400/675°F	600/700°F
Power	kW/shp	32000/42800	32000/42800	38800/52000
Turbine arr.		G(HP+LP)	GG[(HP+GCR)+LP]	GG[(HP+GCR)+LP]
Turbine type		Pa-reaction	GE-impulse	GE-impulse
Turbine speed HP/LP	rev/min	3500/2300	5900/4900	5800/4800
Cruising turbine/propeller speed	rev/min	−/400	10000/400	10000/400
No. of turbine blades		98700	14730	14730
Economiser		No	Yes	Yes
Boiler room		Closed	Open	Open
Feed water system		Half open	Closed	Closed
Range of action at 15 knots	naut.miles	8700	~10000	10500

passed the superheater. By apportioning the fuel in the two furnaces, the superheat temperature could be controlled constant, fig. 9. In the 'Somers' class destroyers, the high temperatures caused trouble, which was the reason why the Bureau of Engineering reduced the superheat to 370° (700°F).

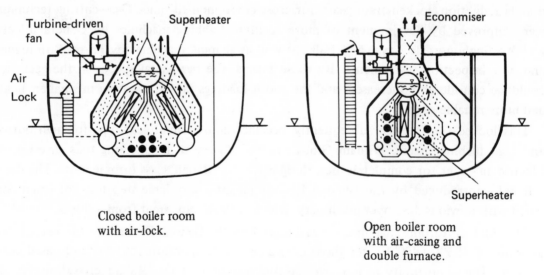

Closed boiler room with air-lock.

Open boiler room with air-casing and double furnace.

Fig. 9. Superheat temperature control in open boiler rooms was introduced for the first time in the 'Benson' destroyers of 1935.

Temperature control was first introduced in the 'Benson' class of 1939, which had double furnace boilers and steam data of 42 bar (600 lb/in²) and 455°C (850°F). This gave a 7 to 20 per cent improvement in fuel economy and range.

With the approach of the Second World War, the U.S. Navy was ready with proven new designs for both boilers and turbines. For quality, availability and efficiency, these were far superior to those of any other nation. The forty-two destroyers of the 'Benson' class were followed during the mass-production of the war years by more than 340 'Fletcher' and 'Summer' destroyers with considerably greater displacement, and powers up to 45 000 kW (60 000 shp). Commencing with the 'Benson' destroyers, steam data was standardized to 42 bar (600 lb/in^2) and 455°C (850°F).

The new alloy steels for superheater tubes, piping and the hot parts of the turbines were sensitive, and new welding procedures had to be developed. These, however, were already fully realized and proven on land. It was the problems with astern manoeuvring and rapid load changes at sea that had to be overcome. For example, the deaerating heaters inherited from land power stations gave trouble initially during rapid load changes. During a crash stop, the pressure in them sank causing the feed pumps to lose suction. The consequences were tripping and blackouts. Sea-going crews were traditionally conservative and needed a long time to learn how to handle the new systems for feed water treatment and control.

Fig. 10 shows the schematic steam cycle for destroyers, initiated with the 'Mahan' class, and the arrangement of boilers, turbines, condenser and feed water equipment, including the deaerator.

When the first battleships were to be built after the First World War, there was considerable (even if not entirely satisfactory) operating experience from destroyers with the higher steam conditions. In 1937, when the battleships 'North Carolina' and 'Washington' were to be ordered, a tiresome conflict arose between 'The Engineers', represented by Admiral Bowen, and those whom he christened 'The Mossbacks', represented by the board of the Marine Department. The 'Mossbacks' were well suported by the 'Big Three', which consisted of the shipyards Bethlehem Steel, Newport News and New York Shipbuilding.

These companies had their own engine workshops and had been building Parsons turbines for more than 20 years. They did not have access to the highly developed technology needed for the high speed turbines, and which was virtually a must for operation with steam conditions of 42 bar (600 lb/in^2) and 455°C (850°F). They were reluctant to let the turbine

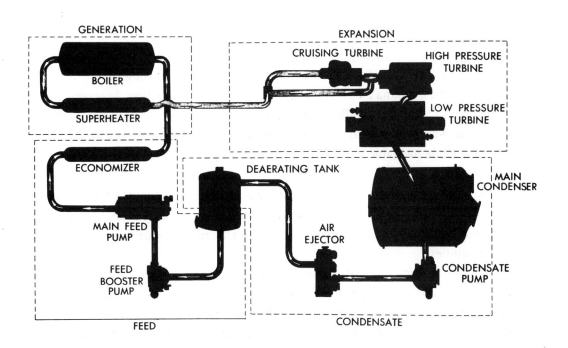

Fig. 10. Steam flow diagram for the 'Mahan' destroyers and their successors.

specialists, General Electric and Westinghouse, take over an important part of their production. It did not help when 'The Engineers' pointed out that the range of action with modern steam data and high speed turbines would be 8 to 10 per cent higher, that the machinery would be considerably lighter and the ship's speed more than one knot higher. After a long struggle, during which Admiral Bowen was made to step down, an investigating commission was formed. This visited a number of land-based power stations with steam conditions of 84 bar (1200 lb/in^2) and 480° (900°F). On the basis of experience from these, the two battleships were finally equipped with high speed General Electric turbines with double reduction gears and steam condition of 42 bar (600 lb/in^2) and 455°C (850°F). Steam turbine development in the U.S. Navy battleships is summarized in Table 4.

Table 4.

Development of battleship machinery in the U.S. Navy.
Inter-war period and the Second World War.

Launch year Deliv. year	Class Tonnage	No.	Power/1000 kW	shp	Speed knots	No. of shafts	Mach arr.	Steam cond. bar/°C lb/in^2/°F
1920–21 1921–23	Maryland 32 600	4	21.6	28,9	21	4	2TG+4EM GE W	19 sat 265/sat
1940 1941	North-Carolina 37 500	2	90	121	28	4	GG(HP+LP) GE	42/455°C 600/850°F
1941–42 1942	South Dakota 40 000	4	97	130	28	4	GG(HP+LP) GE W	42/455°C 600/850°F
1942–44 1943–44	Iowa 48 100	4 (6)	158	212	32	4	GG(HP+LP) GE W	42/455°C 600/850°F

TG = Turbo-generator
EM = Electric motor
sat = saturated steam

GG(HP+LP) = double reduction, locked-train, cross-compound turbine.

In all, it took five years for the new technology to break through from the 'Mahan' destroyers to 'North Carolina'. This development in the U.S. Navy was, however, a unique case of pioneering, and had no parallel in any other fighting fleet until long after the end of the Second World War. For merchant navy machinery it was likewise epoch-making, as the experience was made available to it through the Maritime Administration set up towards the end of the thirties.

This organisation had the task of building up an American merchant fleet with economically driven steamships. These ships were intended for the anticipated world war, and proved their worth when the Japanese attack on Pearl Harbour forced the United States into the hostilities.

The new battleships did not, however, have cruising turbines, but were equipped with four single cross-compound units with double reduction locked-train gears. Cruising power in these battleships was higher than that of the destroyers, and at low powers they could operate on only two shafts. There were insufficient economic and strategic advantages in this type of ship to outweigh the complications of having a cruising turbine.

In the battleship classes 'South Dakota' and 'Iowa', built during the war, the propulsive powers were increased to $4 \times 24\,200$ kW (130 000 shp) and $4 \times 40\,000$ kW (212 000 shp) respectively. The four ships of the 'Iowa' class, which were ready at the end of the War, showed clearly that the enormous costs did not buy a corresponding battleworthiness. The tragic fate of the British battleships, 'King George V' and 'Prince of Wales', in the struggle against the Japanese in 1941, showed the vulnerability of the these mammoth ships against airborne torpedoes and bombs. The planned 'Montana' class of six ships of over 60 000 tons was thus cancelled just prior to the end of hostilities before they were even launched.

From experiences during the First World War, the U.S. Navy realized very early, just as did the British Navy, the enormous importance of ship-based aircraft during fleet movements under war conditions on the high seas. The British converted a 15000 ton passenger ship which became the first aircraft carrier with a deck for take-off and landing. The 'Argus' was completed in 1918 and gave valuable experience. The U.S. Navy was not slow in following with the conversion of a 20000 ton collier, 'Jupiter', from 1913, which was equipped with the first turbo-electric machinery (see Part I). The 'Jupiter' was completed as an aircraft carrier in 1921. The Washington and London treaties allowed no space for the giant U.S. battlecruisers 'Lexington' and 'Saratoga' (nor for the somewhat smaller British battlecruisers 'Furious' and 'Courageous'). These very large cruisers with high speeds were all converted to aircraft carriers. The British ships were ready first, from 1918 to 1925, and the Americans followed somewhat later from 1927 to 1928.

The first US aircraft carrier, designed as such from the very beginning, was 'Ranger', delivered in 1934 (see Table 5). The corresponding British ship, 'Hermes', of 11 000 tons, had by then been in service for ten years, The 'Ranger' could thus be built using experience gained from the British ship. The tonnage was 17600 tons, and machinery of 2×20000 kW (53500 shp) gave her a speed of 29.5 knots. The carrier, however, proved too slow and too unsteady a platform for airplanes to take-off and land. The 'Ranger's' turbines were single reduction, cross-compound units with Curtis high-pressure turbines, and Parsons low-pressure turbines. The three ensuing aircraft carriers of the 'Yorktown' class were therefore given a considerably increased tonnage, 19900 tons, and a machinery of 4×22500 kW (120000 shp) which gave them a speed of 32.5 knots. The main turbines were of the Parsons type in a cross-compound arrangement with single reduction gears.

Delivered in 1940, the 'Wasp' was already at her conception in 1935 unsatisfactory in respect of tonnage (14 500 t.) and power. This was because the 'Yorktown' class had used up such a large part of the U.S. Navy's quota under the Washington treaty that a full size 'Wasp' could not be built without exceeding the limits.

When the 'Essex' class was decided upon in 1940, however, there were no longer any limitations as regards tonnage. 'Essex' and her twentyfour sisters became, therefore, the first fully-grown aircraft carrier designs. They were of 27200 tons, and had machinery of 4×28000 kw (150000 shp) which was sufficient for a speed of 32 1/2 knots. The turbine order was placed with Westinghouse, who designed their first impulse turbines modelled on the example of General Electric. Steam data was brought up to the standard values of the forties, and the machinery was equipped with double reduction gears. It was the torpedo planes and bomber planes from the 'Essex' class that gave the Unites States the decisive weapon in the fight against the Japanese in the Pacific Ocean.

They were, however, extremely expensive and time-consuming to build. The war in the Pacific demanded rapid and large efforts. On the order of the President, the nine cruisers of

Table 5.

**Development of turbine machinery for aircraft carriers in the U.S. Navy.
Inter-war period and Second World War.**

Launch year Deliv. year	Class Tonnage	No.	Power/1000 kW	shp	Speed knots	No. of shafts	Mach. arr.	Steam cond. bar/°C lb/in²/°F
1925 1927	Lexington 37700	2	134	180	33	4	2TG+4EM GE W	21/260°C 290/500°F
1933 1934	Ranger 17600	1	40	53,5	29.5	2	G[(HP+GCR)+LP] Cu+Pa	29/360°C 400/675°F
1936–40 1937–41	Yorkstown 19900	3	89.5	120	32.5	4	G(HP+LP) Pa	29/360°C 400/675°C
1939 1940	Wasp 14700	1	52.5	70	29.5	2	G(HP+LP) Pa	29/360°C 400/675°F
1942–45 1942–46	Essex 27200	25	112	150	32.5	4	GG(HP+LP) W	42/455°C 600/850°F
1942–43 1943	Independence 10700	9	74.6	100	32	4	GG(HP+LP)4 GE	42/455°C 600/850°F
1944–45 1944–46	Commencement Bay 18700	19	11.9	16	19	2	GG(HP+LP) A C	42/455°C 600/850°F
1945–46 1945–47	Midway 47400	3	158	212	33	4	GG(HP+LP) W GE	42/455°C 600/850°F
1945 1946	Saipan 14500	2	89.5	120	35	4	GG(HP+LP) GE	42/455°C 600/850°F

W = Westinghouse
GE = General Electric
AC = Allis Chalmers
Cu = Curtis
Pa = Parsons

GG(HP+LP) = double reduction, locked-train, cross-compound turbine

G(HP+LP) = single reduction, cross-compound turbine

G[(HP+GCR)+LP] = single reduction, cross-compound turbine, with cruising turbine geared to HP

TG = turbo-generator
EM = electric motor

the 'Cleveland' class were converted to aircraft carriers and named after the lead ship, 'Independence'. These carried out exceedingly important duties during the years of crisis in the Pacific, 1943 to 1945.

As an aftermath to the Pearl Harbour catastrophe, four giant aircraft carriers of the 'Midway' class with a displacement of 47400 tons were ordered. These were to have machinery of 4×39600 kW (212000 shp) and make 33 knots. Six of these giant ships were ordered, but three were cancelled before the end of the war. These large turbine units were also built by Westinghouse and General Electric. The large tonnage gave the designers a chance to protect both hangars and flight deck with proper armour. These ships were admittedly extraordinarily expensive, and never managed to face the Japanese in battle. As well as these giant ships, a large number of escort aircraft carriers were built during the final phases of the war, all of which were steam-driven. Among these escort carriers, a whole series of about fifty ships with steam reciprocating engines was built.

2.2 Some turbine designs in the U.S. Navy
during the thirties and forties

Reaction Turbines

The period after the First World War was one of difficult adjustment for U.S. shipyards and manufacturers of marine machinery. During the war, all workshops had been full to capacity, whether they built reaction or impulse turbines. About as many of each type had been made. Several yards built Parsons turbines in their engine shops under licence from the Parsons Marine Steam Turbine Company. In a rapidly shrinking market, it was obvious that the yards would attempt to fill their own workshops rather than order from the turbine companies of General Electric, Westinghouse, de Laval and Allis Chalmers.

The turbine designs made by the yards were based upon drawings and data from the licenser. Machinery was therefore similar to the British single reduction, cross-compound types with a Curtis wheel as governing stage, followed by reaction drums. The rotors were solid-forged drums in a single piece at one end of the shaft, with a shaft-end forming the governing wheel and dummy piston fastened to the other end of the drum by a shrink-fit and bolts. Such a high pressure rotor is shown by Fig. 8. The low pressure turbines were generally a drum design with a double exhaust. The astern turbine, arranged at one end of the low pressure turbine had one or more Curtis stages with, in some cases, a reaction section to follow. The designs were modelled very closely on the corresponding British units from Parsons which are reviewed in Chapter 3.

Westinghouse had acquired, as early as 1895, a licence from C.A. Parsons & Co for their land turbines. This company was quite separate from the Parsons Marine Steam Turbine Co. When George Westinghouse decided to develop ships' machinery based upon John McAlpine's gear designs (with 'Neptune' as the first installation between 1911 to 1912) he started from C.A. Parsons & Co's basic designs for turbines, but proceeded otherwise in his own way, see Part I, page 112. From the very start, Westinghouse's design used a Curtis wheel as a governing stage, followed by reaction drums. During the First World War, Westinghouse delivered over twenty cross-compound destroyer units, with powers of about 2×9000 kW (24000 shp) to the U.S. Navy.

Westinghouse developed early his own system for attaining good efficiencies, both at cruising and full speeds. For warships, where cruising powers were normally only a fraction of the full speed power, Westinghouse used a separate cruising turbine which normally took the whole heat drop and the entire steam flow, and was provided with an astern turbine. At higher powers, a bypass valve was opened, which released steam from the governing stage to a separate parallel turbine. This was connected at higher speeds but rotated unloaded in vacuum at cruising speeds. The first larger ships equipped with such an arrangement were the Swedish iron-clads 'Gustav V' and 'Drottning Viktoria' 1920 and 1921, described in Part I, page 72.

A more sophisticated version of this system, with a parallel turbine for full speed, was delivered by Westinghouse in 1933 to the four 'New Orleans' class cruisers. The power was $4 \times 20\,000$ kW (107000 shp), steam pressure 20 bar (275 lb/in^2) and 300°C (575°F) superheat. The turbine arrangement is shown by Fig. 11. The cruising turbine and the parallel turbine were disposed in a modified cross-compound arrangement. Both stood directly upon the common condenser, a great advance upon the designs of the twenties that had their condensers to the side or placed separately with large and bulky steam exhaust pipes

23

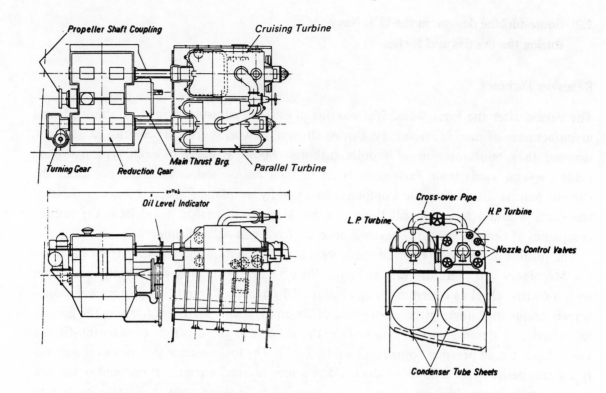

Fig. 11. The Westinghouse design for the 'New Orleans' crusiers. Cruising and parallel turbines with three steam flows, 1933. Power 20 000 kW (26 800 shp). Steam data 20 bar, 300°C (275 lb/in², 575°F). Speed 3 800/360 rev/min.

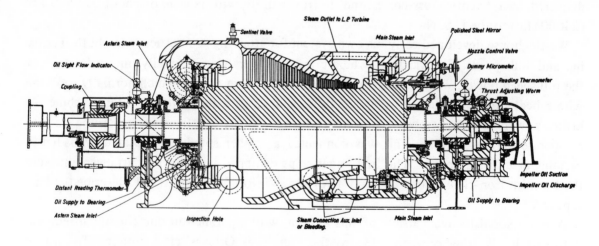

Fig. 12. Cruising turbine for the 'New Orleans' class, with the astern turbine supported free of the outer casing, and auxiliary steam inlet, or bleeding, connections. Speed, 3 800 rev/min.

to the condenser room. The single casing cruising turbine, fig. 12, was complete with a Curtis governing stage, reaction section with exhaust to the condenser and astern turbine.

The rotor had a relatively high speed, and was made from a single, solid forging. The blading was a two-row Curtis stage followed by twentyfive rows of moving blades in the reaction section. The astern turbine was only a two-row Curtis stage. It is interesting to note here that the astern turbine stands by itself in the low pressure casing, and there is an extra guide vane after the Curtis stage. This design was clearly in advance of its time. When opened to hot astern steam, the astern casing could expand freely without causing any dangerous internal stresses or distortions. The extra vane guided the exhaust steam from the astern turbine to flow in the same direction as the steam from the ahead turbine's last stage blades. This was a clear benefit and reduced the ahead turbine's tendency to run hot during astern operation.

At higher powers, a bypass valve was opened in the cross-over pipe between the governing stage exhaust chamber and the two central steam inlets of the parallel turbine. The steam inlet in the upper casing led the steam to a nozzle group where it expanded through the single impulse wheel, see fig. 13. From there, the steam passed through ten rows of moving blades in the parallel turbine's after reaction section and down to the condenser. An equal amount of steam to the lower casing expanded through nozzle groups with an opposite direction of flow through the impulse wheel and further through its reaction section to the condenser. At full speed, the cruising turbine and the parallel turbine gave approximately the same power and had the same speed of 3800 rev/min. The condenser thus received three steam flows. The design was compact, but the steam consumption, especially at cruising speeds, was not particularly favourable. At cruising speeds, the steam only passed through the cruising turbine.

If heat drop per kg steam is the same at cruising as at full power, then the blade speed ratio would be only half full power value. If the efficiency at full speed was optimized, the

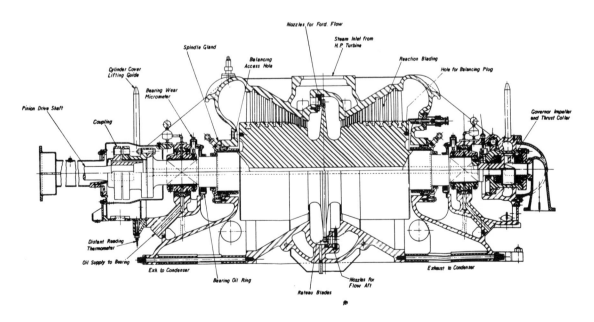

Fig. 13. Parallel LP turbine for the 'New Orleans' class with Rateau impulse stage and opposite flow directions in the upper and lower half casings, double flow rotor with no astern turbine. Speed, 3 800 rev/min.

efficiency at cruising speeds would be rather bad. The high turbine speeds, the solid rotors and the separate astern casing were, however, important advances compared with the Parsons turbines built by the large shipyards. Ingress of auxiliary steam from the auxiliary turbines to the governing stage chamber, or to the middle of the reaction drum in the cruising turbine, gave an important contribution to the power at low loads.

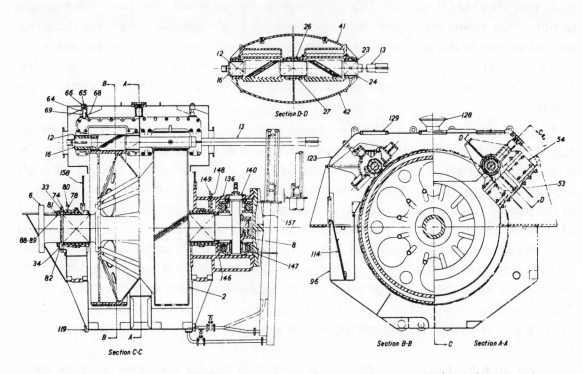

Fig. 14. Westinghouse gear for the 'New Orleans' cruisers. Output, 20000 kW/shaft (26800 shp). Speeds, 4900/3800/380 rev/min.

Fig. 14 shows a section through the gear. The casing was welded from plate, and the cast steel bearing brackets were welded into the casing; it was probably the first wholly-welded gear casing of its kind ever. The pinions were supported by MacAlpine's floating frames, and the turbines were coupled to the pinions by long torsion shafts. The wheel rims were welded to web plates, which were welded to flanges on the propeller shaft and were additionally strengthened by inclined tubular spokes. As the reduction ratio was in excess of ten to one, a three-bearing support of the pinions was necessary to keep the deflection within acceptable limits. The tooth loadings were very high for those days, 9.3 bar (135 lb/in^2).

2.3 General Electric high speed turbines for high steam pressures and temperatures

As already described in the previous section, the pioneering efforts of Gibbs & Cox and the General Electric for the 'Mahan' destroyer machinery resulted in new prototypes for the subsequent destroyers, cruisers and battleships in the U.S. Fleet. The designs and systems were likewise in due time epoch-making for turbine development in merchant ships too. Fig. 15 compares the dimensions of the high pressure rotors for the 'Farragut' class of 1932 (A) and the 'Mahan' class of 1933 (B). The 'Mahan' rotor ran at 5900 rev/min compared with 'Farragut's' 3500 rev/min. The 'Mahan' rotor had a Curtis stage and eleven moving blade rows, while the 'Farragut' had a Curtis stage and twenty-nine rows of blades. The number of moving blades was 1750 compared with 17500 on the 'Farragut', and the entire 'Mahan' unit had about 15000 blades while the corresponding number on the 'Farragut' was almost 100 000. The efficiency of the 'Farragut' unit was 5 to 10 % worse.

It can easily be appreciated that the warming-through time for the 'Farragut' rotor with its shrink fits was several times longer than for the 'Mahan' gashed-type solid rotor which weighed only half as much.

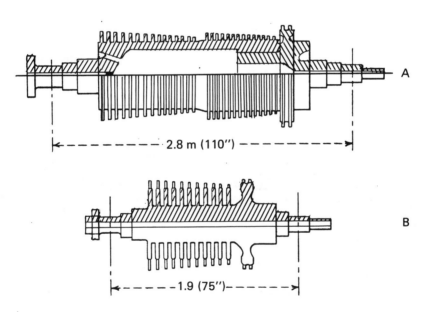

Fig. 15. Comparison between the high pressure rotors of the 'Farragut' and 'Mahan' destroyers. Shaft power 8000 kW (10720 shp), speed 3500 and 5900 rev/min, respectively. Number of blades 17500 and 1750.

Fig. 16 shows a section through 'Mahan's cruising turbine, cruising gear and h.p. turbine. The separate cruising turbines, which always rotated, made possible an increase in range for the 'Mahan' destroyers of 10 per cent. The new valve arrangement with three nozzle valves in the cruising turbine and as many in the h.p. turbine, plus two bypass valves reduced the specific steam consumption at part loads.

The double-flow type low pressure turbine, fig. 17, had a solid rotor with gashed-out discs for the impulse stages. The astern turbine with one Curtis wheel was situated in the forward part of the low-pressure casing in a separate thermo-elastic casing. The low-pressure casing was an all-welded design with strong side beams integral with the exhaust casing. The condenser hung from these beams. The upper half of the low-pressure casing was a

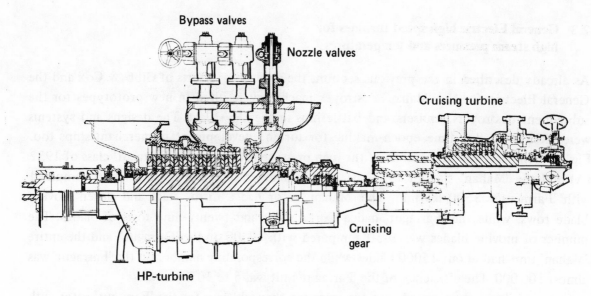

Fig. 16. High pressure turbine and geared cruising turbine of the 'Mahan'. Speed 5900 and 10000 rev/min, 29 bar, 360°C (400 lb/in², 675°F). (Designed for 42 bar, 455°C (600 lb/in², 850°F).)

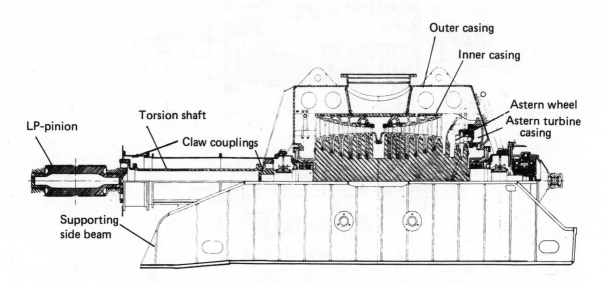

Fig. 17. Low pressure turbine of the 'Mahan' with welded casing and strong side-beams carrying the casing and condenser. Separate single-flow astern turbine. Torsion shaft and claw-type couplings. Speed 4900 rev/min.

light plate cover intended only to withstand the atmospheric pressure while the inner cylinder resisted the steam pressure. Long, flexible torsion shafts allowed movement between the gear and low pressure rotors, whilst minimizing angular displacements in the claw-type couplings which ran in oil.

The low-pressure turbines in the 'Mahan' class had a propensity for local overheating during high and protracted astern powers with poor vacuum. Steam from the astern turbine was sucked into the ahead blading. In the last stage of the after flow the temperature rose so high during such operating conditions that the casing deformed and the blades overheated.

To avoid this phenomenon, all low pressure turbines, whether for destroyers, cruisers or battleships, built after the 'Mahan' class had double astern turbines working in parallel.

Fig. 18 shows the manoeuvring gear in the destroyer classes following the 'Mahan' class. The live steam from the boilers passed through a steam strainer whose purpose was to protect the turbines from particles deriving from the piping. After this was an emergency trip valve, which was a safety device to shut off the steam in the event of overspeed, low lube oil pressure or faulty rotor position.

During cruising speeds, the steam went to the three nozzle valves of the cruising turbine which were opened sequentially by turning the cruising turbine's handwheel. Exhaust steam from the cruising turbine passed a cross-over valve to an uncontrolled nozzle group in the high pressure turbine and thence through the following impulse stages and on to the low pressure turbine. The bypass valves on the high pressure turbine were shut during cruising powers. With demand for high powers, live steam was admitted sequentially through the three nozzle valves of the high pressure turbine.

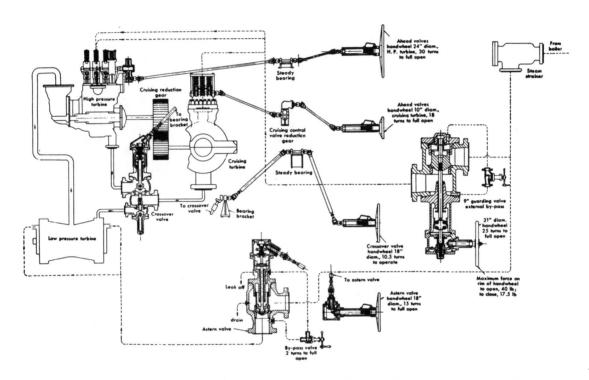

Fig. 18. Manoeuvring arrangement on destroyers of the 'Somers' class and ensuing ships with separate geared cruising turbines.

As the pressure in the casing downstream of the Curtis stage rose, the three bypass valves were opened accordingly. The high pressure turbine nozzle valves and bypass valves were actuated by one and the same handwheel. When the pressure in the high pressure turbine Curtis chamber rose so much that the steam flow in the cruising turbine was reduced, and its efficiency and power decreased, the cross-over valve handwheel was operated. Exhaust steam from the cruising turbine was redirected to the condenser, and its nozzle valves were closed. The cruising turbine then rotated in a vacuum and was cooled by passing a small quantity of live steam through the turbine. A large single-seated control valve for astern operation passed steam to the two Curtis astern wheels in the low pressure turbine and was operated by a separate handwheel.

The extraordinarily successful turbine design of the 'Mahan' class became the prototype for subsequent destroyer, cruiser and battleship machinery. Already in the 'Somers' class destroyers of 1935, the steam pressure was raised to 42 bar (600 lb/in²) and the temperature to 455°C (850°F). These steam conditions had also been the basis for the 'Mahan' turbines, but had never been used as the boiler makers at that time were not so advanced in development. Before the step to 455°C could be taken, boilers had to be developed where the superheat temperature could be kept constant independently of the load. When this was achieved in the 'Somers' class, 42 bar (600 lb/in²) and 455°C (850°F) became standard for the whole of the forties and far into the fifties. As a guinea-pig, a destroyer from the twenties, the 'Dahlgren', was rebuilt in 1939 and fitted out with high pressure, high temperature boilers for 84 bar, 480°C (1200 lb/in², 900°F). The experiment showed that even these steam conditions could be utilized with acceptable reliability.

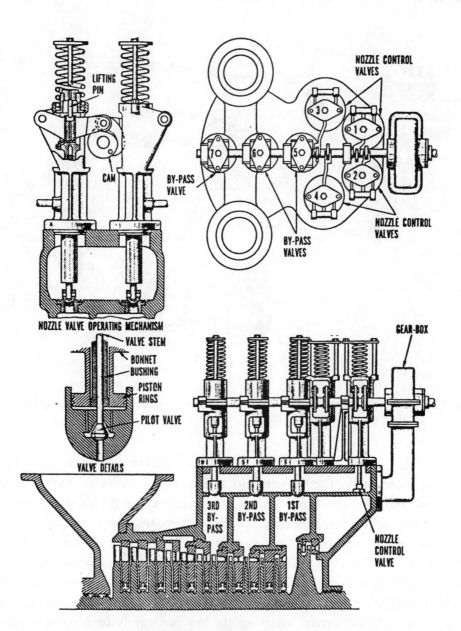

Fig. 19. General Electric arrangement with four nozzle valves and three bypass valves on the high pressure turbines for battleships and cruisers.

The first cruisers to get machinery with high speed turbines and double reduction gears were the 'Cleveland' class of 1939 with standard data of 42 bar, 455°C (600 lb/in², 850°F) and a power of $4 \times 28\,000$ kW (150 000 shp). With four propeller shafts it became apparent that the advantages of cruising turbines were outweighed by costs and complications. Instead, the high pressure turbines were equipped with several nozzle valves and bypass valves.

Fig. 19 shows schematically the valve mechanisms for cruisers and battleships with four nozzle valves and three bypass valves actuated by camshafts from a single handwheel. The opening sequence of the valves was fixed and controlled by the cam profiles and their angular position. Low pressure turbines for cruisers and battleships were in principle enlarged destroyer designs. To achieve better astern powers, the astern turbines were made either as three-row Curtis wheels or double two-row Curtis wheels. The difference between a low pressure reaction turbine of Westinghouse manufacture, fig. 20, and a corresponding turbine of General Electric design, fig. 21, for a battleship was insignificant. The General Electric turbine had six moving blade stages, where the first stage blades were designed with 15 per cent reaction, and the last stage had 40 per cent at the tip and 20 per cent at the bottom. Westinghouse turbines had nine reaction stages and no gashed-type discs. All the blade stages had 50 per cent reaction, and the exhaust-end blades were heavily twisted with a lower degree of reaction at the hub. In battleship machinery of the 'Iowa' class of 1940, the power was $4 \times 39\,500$ kW (212000 shp), and the same machinery was installed in the aircraft carriers of the 'Midway' class from 1941. All this machinery was, broadly speaking, enlarged 'Mahan' turbines.

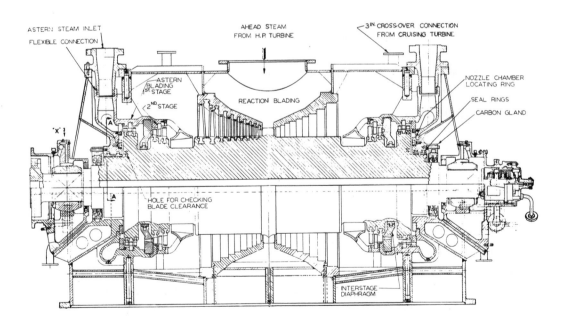

Fig. 20. Westinghouse low pressure turbine for the aircraft carrier 'Essex' with 2×9 reaction stages and two parallel astern turbines, each with two Curtis wheels. $4 \times 28\,000$ kW (150 000 shp) 4 300 rev/min, 42 bar/455°C (600 lb/in², 840°F).

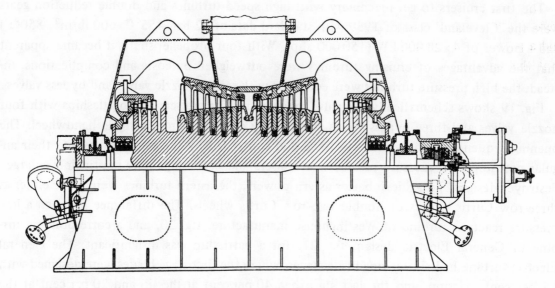

Fig. 21. General Electric low pressure turbine for a battleship, with 2x6 impulse stages and two parallel astern turbines with three-row Curtis wheels.

2.4 Double reduction and locked-train gears from de Laval and General Electric

As is evident from the preceeding material, the proposals of Gibbs and Cox and the Bureau of Ships together with the high speed turbines of the General Electric could only succeed if gears for powers of at least 8 000 kW per shaft (11 000 shp), and speeds of about 6 000 rev/min could be realized. At normal propeller speeds of about 400 rev/min for destroyers, and 300 to 350 rev/min for battleships and cruisers, this necessitated a reduction ratio of up to 20. It was quite impracticable to design such a gear in a single reduction with dimensions that could be used in warships.

In 1933, therefore, the U.S. Navy commissioned the de Laval Steam Turbine Company to attempt, in collaboration with General Electric, a design for a double reduction gear for the 'Mahan' destroyer machinery. Both de Laval and General Electric had built locked-train double reduction gears for merchant ships and low powers. These had proved reliable. Both companies had access to gear-cutting machines of high precision, and had developed methods for measuring tooth profiles and tooth contacts in the mesh. De Laval's chief engineer, Richard Waller, was project leader. In a very short time, prototypes of locked-train gears were produced, which were subjected to comprehensive testing to establish reliable design criteria that could stand up to the tooth loadings and the deformations.

The resulting design from this work is shown in principle by figs. 22 to 25. There were a great number of quite new constructional ideas and new methods of manufacture that made Richard Waller's design so original, not only for the destroyers, cruisers and battleships in the U.S. Navy, but also for the large propulsion engines in the tankers and container ships to come some thirty to forty years later.

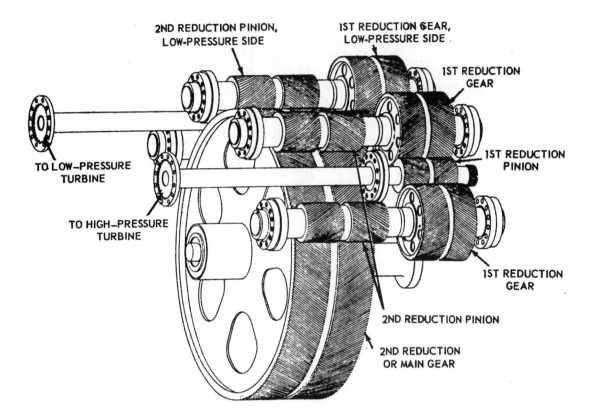

Fig. 22. Locked-train, double reduction gear designed by de Laval and General Electric for the 'Mahan' destroyers of 1933.

1. The torques from the turbines were split into two equal and opposed peripheral forces. The pinion bearing reactions thus became smaller and the bearing surfaces could be reduced. By distributing the torques among four quill shafts and four second reduction pinions, the same diameter of the bull wheel could transmit twice the power compared with 'free-train' gears having two quill shafts.

2. The gear casing was of welded steel plate with cast steel bearing brackets and double side walls which provided very stable supports for the rotors.

3. By transmitting the torques from the first reduction wheels to the second reduction pinions through long torsion shafts supported in flexible couplings, the torques transmitted in the two meshes could more readily be equalized. In addition, movement between the rotors could be assimilated without affecting the meshing of the teeth.

4. The large second reduction wheel was wholly welded from plate, and the gear rim of tempered steel was likewise welded directly to the web plates. A great advance was the development of preheating for the welding, making it possible to weld the tempered rings without local hardness and cracks.

5. The thrust bearing was made integral with the strong gear casing in a single, solid box with gussets connecting down to the double bottom.

6. Comprehensive full-power tests with two gears coupled back-to-back and torqued-up for full load and overload were carried out at Annapolis. The tests showed that gears designed for tooth loads of about $K=7$ bar (100 lb/in^2) could be overloaded up to 50 per cent without damage.

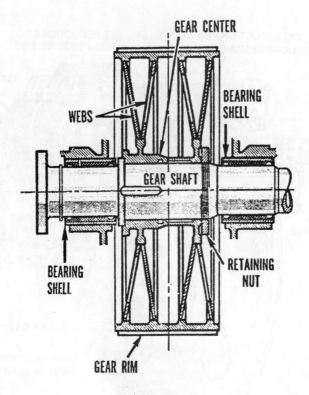

Fig. 23. De Laval wheel construction from 1933 with a welded-on gear rim and shrunk-on propeller shaft.

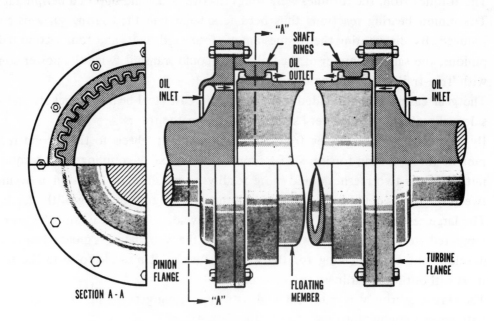

Fig. 24. Flexible coupling for the 'Fast' type with lubricated fine-pitch teeth and a floating torque tube.

7. The older dowel or dog-type coupling between pinions, turbines and wheels was replaced in the destroyer class following the 'Mahan' by fine tooth couplings, fig. 24, patented by a man named Fast, a Swedish-American. With this component, a weak link in turbine machinery was eliminated. Earlier couplings were only reliable with proper alignment between pinion, wheel and turbine shafts. The Fast couplings could accommodate sizeable angular errors without wear. Even today Fast-type couplings are the design most used in high speed marine machinery.

It was to take decades before other navies caught up with the high standard already possessed by the U.S. Navy prior to the Second World War in respect of weight, sound level and reduction ratios. All this was due to the high quality manufacture and superior design of the American gear makers. A classic gear design for a U.S. destroyer from 1944 is shown by fig. 25.

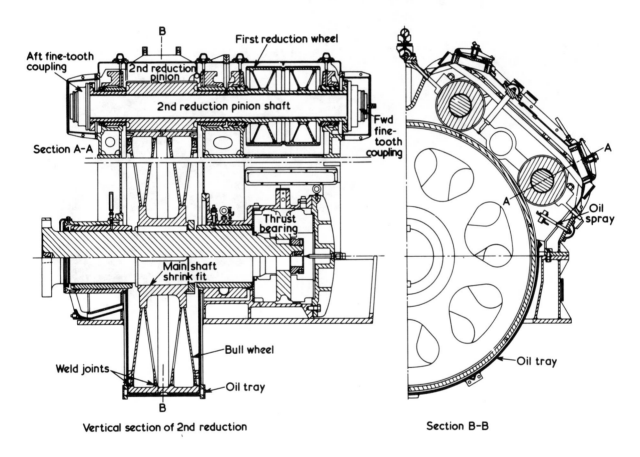

Fig. 25. De Laval locked-train gear for a U.S. destroyer from 1944.
Output, 15 000 kW (20 000 shp).

35

Just how compact a U.S. aircraft carrier machinery of the 'Essex' class from the Second World War was, may be seen from fig. 26. The cruising turbine had triple reduction down to the propeller shaft, reducing the speed from about 10 000 to 300 rev/min.

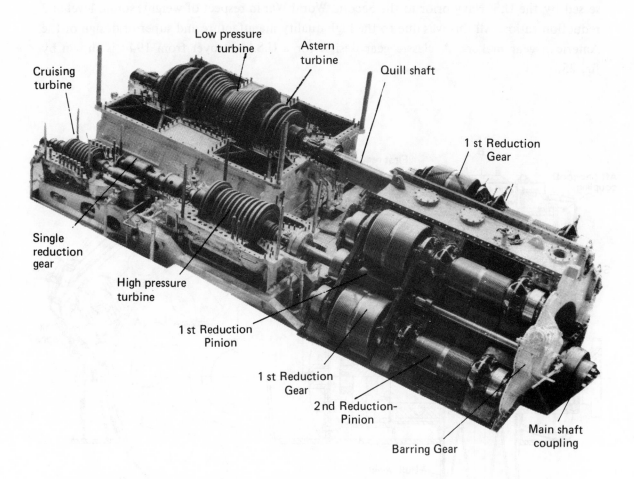

Fig. 26. Aircraft carrier machinery for the 'Essex' class from the Second World War with geared cruising turbine and a double locked-train gear. Power 28 000 kW (37 500 shp).

2.5 Post-War Years – the Fifties, Sixties and Seventies

With the conclusion of the war in 1945, the feverish expansion of the U.S. naval and merchant fleets at shipyards and factories came to an end. But the technological development at the Navy's and the big private companies' testing establishments did not stop. The greater part of the newly-built warships were "mothballed", and it was the time for assimilating war experiences won through costly losses in men and ships. The day of the battleship and battlecruiser was manifestly past. Those huge, expensive hulls, despite all their armour and anti-aircraft defences had shown themselves too vulnerable to submarine torpedoes and the modern aerial torpedoes, bombs and missiles.

Without aircraft carriers and air-cover, an ocean fleet of pre-war type was worthless. New weapons such as guided rockets and missiles had proved their efficacy and did not require such a large hull for a firing platform as did the heavy artillery. On the other hand, aircraft carriers and convoys were extremely vulnerable to submarine torpedoes which were gradually developed for homing or remote control. Revolutionary new weapons and the advent of electronics with sensing, seeing, steering, navigating and programmed systems, made existing ship designs worthless, without extensive and expensive rebuilding to accommodate all the new weapons systems. No new large battleships or battlecruisers with heavy guns as their main armament were built, and many ships already on order were cancelled.

New specialized ships appeared. Destroyers and cruisers were remodelled to suit them to the new weaponry. In this way, the classic destroyers with artillery and torpedoes as main armament had their successors specially designed for the new weapons for air defence, submarine-hunting and fighting surface vessels. The classic destroyers were designated by the letters DD in the U.S. Navy. Attack destroyers with guided missiles as their main armament were now given the letters DDG (G=guided missiles). A large number of ocean-going escort destroyers for protecting aircraft carriers and convoys were called DDE, in the same way that frigates and corvettes for submarine hunting and convoy duty were allocated the letters FF and FFG. The ocean greyhounds that once had speeds up to forty knots became slower. Hulls became less extreme in shape and broader so as to carry all the electronics and weaponry on deck without jeopardising stability. Cruisers and destroyers detailed for protecting aircraft carriers, however, retained the demand to be able to match the carrier's 32 to 35 knots, even in heavy seas, The development can be gathered from Tables 6, 7 and 8 (pages 46, 47, and 48).

Aircraft carriers grew in size and power. The 'Midway' class of 1945 to 1946, had already passed the 33 000 tons and 133 000 kW (180 000 shp) of the old 'Lexington' and 'Saratoga'. The later ships of the 'Forrestal' and the new 'Saratoga' classes of 1956 to 1960 were even bigger, reaching a displacement of 60 000 up to 80 000 tons and an installed engine power of 4×52 200 kW (280 000 shp).

The size of aircraft carriers increased even more with the introduction of nuclear propulsion in the 'Enterprise' and 'Nimitz' classes. These did not, however, have increased propulsive power over that of the 'Forrestal' class. The total domination of aircraft carrier development in the U.S. Navy viewed internationally is a direct consequence of the United States' strategic position on the high seas. Up until the 'Enterprise' class, the machinery was oil-fired, but was thereafter replaced by nuclear-driven plants. This class had eight smaller reactors, while the 'Nimitz' class could produce a total power of 209 000 kW (280 000 shp) from two large reactors only. All these ships had four shafts and turbine units. For the 'Nimitz' ships under construction, the engine powers have not officially been exceeded.

The American aircraft carriers have undergone an impressive development, but changes in the airforce have been even more radical. The jet engine has brought a revolution both for land-based and sea-borne aircraft. The Soviet Navy's rapid and unexpected expansion during the fifties and sixties has meant that the United States considered it justified substantially to increase their own naval fleet from the seventies on. The advent of helicopters for submarine hunting and reconnaissance, as well as jet aircraft with short take-off and landing distances, known as STOL and VTOL aircraft,* has signified a completely new line of development for aircraft-carrying ships as well. For this reason, neither the Soviet nor British navies have considered it economically justified to follow the United States line and develop giant aircraft carriers.

While the developments at the end of hostilities have been completely revolutionary with regard to weapons, they have perhaps been less dramatic for turbines, although even there considerable advances have been made. Quite early, the U.S. Navy built two special experimental destroyers to try out new types of machinery. As already stated, the pre-war destroyer, 'Dahlgren', was rebuilt during the war and equipped with machinery that comprised boilers and turbines for high steam conditions 84 bar (1 200 lb/in²) and 480°C (900°F). Relatively few difficulties occurred with this machinery. In the 'Gearing' class of 1945 to 1946 the destroyer 'Timmerman' was used for comprehensive testing. She was fitted with two different machineries, one on each shaft with a power of 37 300 kW (50 000 shp). The machinery on one side had boilers of 139 bar (2 000 lb/in²) and 565°C (1 050°F). The other shaft unit was designed for 70 bar (1 000 lb/in²) and 565°C (1 050°F). 'Timmerman' showed, however, that machinery development could not be advanced by too large steps and too radical designs without compromising reliability. The experience, however, was sufficiently positive as regards boilers and turbines that the Navy decided to standardize steam conditions of 84 bar, 510°C (1 200 lb/in², 950°F) for all larger surface vessels, starting with the 'Mitscher' class of 1952 to 1954. For the turbine designers, these data were not difficult to utilize because they had wide experience on land installations with steam conditions up to 240 bar (3 500 lb/in²) and 565°C (1 050°F).

The boiler makers found that the complicated double furnaces could be discarded. By a suitable arrangement of the radiation and convection surfaces of the superheaters it became apparent that an adequately constant superheat temperature could be obtained over a large power range. The resulting simpler furnace space made the boiler considerably smaller and lighter. The turbine-driven boiler fans were designed for a forced draught pressure of up to 1.3 metres water (50'') head, about twice that of the boilers of the forties. In that way, the steam generation at full speed could be increased, thus allowing a corresponding reduction of machinery weight and space.

The turbine designers built further upon experience gained during the war. The insensitivity of impulse rotors to rapid temperature changes had already been noted. With the change to 455°C superheat temperature, the Navy decreed that only impulse rotors were to be used for high pressure turbines. For low pressure turbines, impulse and reaction blading were almost equally good.

At the beginning of the fifties, General Electric made an important advance in ship's turbines. Since the days of Parsons and de Laval, it had been an established rule that over-criti-

---

* STOL = *S*hort *T*ake *Off* and *L*anding

  VTOL = *V*ertical *T*ake *Off* and *L*anding

cal rotors were not to be used for operation in ships, where speeds were changing during manoeuvring from maximum ahead to astern. A ship's turbine must be capable of running at all speeds, and from the beginning it had been deemed impossible to have a rotor with its critical speed within the operating range. Over-critical rotors, as introduced by Gustav de Laval, could be accepted for constant speed machines where one could quickly pass through the critical speed. Naval authorities and classification societies, therefore, laid down that rotors for shipboard installations should have their critical speeds at least 30 per cent higher than the highest operating speed.

Around 1948/49 General Electric's experts found, during checks of vibration conditions for a number of low pressure rotors, that due to erroneous assumptions in the calculations, the rotors actually had their natural frequencies within the operating range in some cases. The rotors had certainly shown a tendency to vibrate within the natural frequency range, but only in those cases where the balancing had been poor.

The research report that General Electric published in the Transactions of Naval Architects and Marine Engineers in 1951 proved that the traditional methods of calculation for critical speeds were quite wrong for larger rotors (Reference 72). Up to then, no account had been taken of the fact that the bearings were in reality not at all stiff and inelastically supported as the calculations assumed. Both the bearing brackets and the oil films were elastic. Because of this, nodes did not occur at the bearing centres as supposed by the calculations. The rotor's effective length between the nodes was therefore considerably greater than the distance between the bearings.

The result was that the critical speeds in the rotors investigated were up to 40 to 50 per cent lower than those calculated using the stiff-bearing model. What was most interesting in the report was that the rotors displayed quite acceptable vibration levels over the entire operating range, even when they ran within the critical speed area.

Brown Boveri had made the same error in their critical speed calculations, and had arrived at the same conclusion as General Electric already before W.W.2. During thorough vibration measurements in a test rig of a couple of their large low pressure marine rotors in 1938, it was found that the critical speeds were at about full power speed. This condition, however, did not disturb the operation as long as the rotors were well balanced.

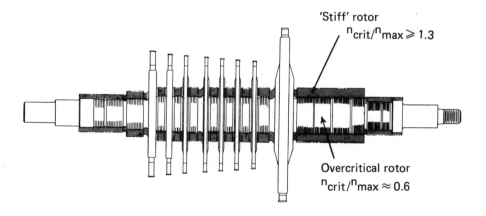

'Stiff' rotor
$n_{crit}/n_{max} \geqslant 1.3$

Overcritical rotor
$n_{crit}/n_{max} \approx 0.6$

Fig. 27. Over-critical and under-critical marine high pressure rotors as calculated by General Electric in 1951.

General Electric decided at the beginning of the fifties to design their marine rotors deliberately for a critical speed at about 60 per cent of the full speed. With over-critical rotors considerable advantages were won in this way. These were especially great for high pressure rotors, where their slimness made it possible to reduce leakages and raise efficiencies. In the low pressure rotors, where leakage losses were not so important, the gains from over-critical rotors were of less significance. How this new design principle affected the dimensions of a high pressure rotor is shown by fig. 27.

One condition that an over-critical rotor could be run at its critical speed without troublesome vibrations, however, was that the balancing was adequate and that the bearings gave sufficient damping. It was found that it was not enough to balance the rotor statically and at low speed. The rotor was usually balanced by adding balance weights or removing material from the two turbine discs nearest to the bearings. If the balance weights on the outer discs compensated for an unbalance at the centre of the rotor, the rotor ran vibration-free at low speeds. At high speeds, however, the unbalance forces deflected the rotor shaft so that it bent and could cause unacceptable vibration amplitudes, when passing through the natural frequency.

Over-critical rotors must, therefore, be balanced in at least three planes instead of two, and in addition should preferably be balanced at full speed. It was also found that solid-forged rotors must be thermally stable so as not to be bend at the high steam temperatures they were subjected to. General Electric therefore introduced heat stability rotation tests quite early as a standard check on their solid rotors. In this way, it was ensured that thermally stable rotors were obtained.

Using over-critical rotors in marine service, cruising turbine speeds could be raised from 10 000 rev/min to 12 000 or 18 000 rev/min, and high pressure rotor speeds from 5000 or 6000 rev/min to 7000 and 9000 rev/min. Low pressure turbine speeds were also raised to 5000 and 6000 rev/min. With these high speeds and smaller diameters, higher efficiencies were attained, and at the same time rotors and turbines became smaller and lighter. Larger heat drops could be utilized in each blading stage and the number of stages could be reduced. In addition, use was made of the considerable improvement in propulsive efficiency achievable at lower propeller speeds. Beginning in the fifties, therefore, propeller speeds were reduced by about 50 rev/min, both for cruisers and destroyers.

Earlier on, Parsons had used a series-parallel steam connection of high and intermediate pressure turbines for some of his direct-driven turbine installations. During cruising speeds, these had passed steam from the high pressure turbine to the intermediate pressure turbine, and thence to the low pressure turbine. At full speed, both the high pressure and intermediate pressure turbines received live steam directly, and the exhaust steam flows from both turbines went to the following low pressure turbine. The U.S. Navy had tested series-parallel connections of geared turbines with three rotors in a number of destroyers during the First World War with some success. The Japanese cruiser 'Kuma' with a power of 4× 16 700 kW (90 000 shp) had high and intermediate pressure turbines with series-parallel connection already in 1927. The German manufacturer, Krupp-Germaniawerft, patented such a system in 1933 with a combined high pressure and intermediate pressure rotor in tandem. This design was used by the German Navy in a number of their destroyers built before and during the war.

Brown Boveri built four units from 1939 to 1940 with a record designed output of 57 400 kW (77 000 shp) per shaft with a series-parallel arrangement. This was calculated to give considerable advantages, both at cruising and full speeds (see Section 5.5, Part 2). The U.S. Reparations Commission that visited Germany after the war to collect machinery designs of value brought little of interest home with them. The only design they found really interesting was the series-parallel arrangement as used in the German destroyers.

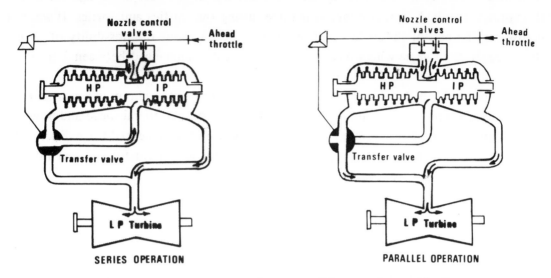

Fig. 28. Diagrammatic arrangement of series-parallel connection used by the U.S. Navy, beginning with the 'Mitscher' destroyers of 1952.

Series–parallel arrangements were therefore put into service, starting with the 'Mitscher' class destroyers of 1952. They had an output of $2 \times 30\,000$ kW (80 000 shp) and were rebuilt during the period of 1966 to 1969 as missile destroyers. The arrangement, fig. 28, was definitely simpler than previous installations with geared cruising turbines, and proved to have considerable advantages. Fig. 29 shows 'Mitscher's series-parallel turbine with a common rotor for high and intermediate pressure blading. A number of U.S. aircraft carriers have also been fitted with turbine units of series-parallel arrangement, see Tables 6 and 7.

Fig. 29. High pressure turbine for cruisers with a series-parallel arrangement of high and intermediate pressure blading (Westinghouse).

One condition that elevated turbine speeds and reduced propeller speeds could be utilized was, however, that the gearing could be built with sufficiently high reduction ratios. It had already proved necessary to use triple reduction for the 'Mahan' destroyers' cruising turbines, which had a speed of 10 000 rev/min. If these high speeds of the high pressure turbines were to be utilized, far higher peripheral speeds were needed in the gear mesh, and far higher tooth-loadings than had been considered feasible during the thirties and forties. It was not until towards the end of the forties that discussions began about the possibility of raising the tooth-loadings of gears which had remained practically unchanged between 7 to 9 bar (100 to 130 lb/in^2) for more than twenty years.

It was pointed out in Part I, page 41, that the dimensions of the pinion in a gear unit are mainly, dependent upon the specific tooth load, the K-factor, peripheral speed and power.

The K-factor expresses the surface pressure resulting from the tangential force distributed across the axial tooth length of the pinion, with a correction factor for the gear ratio as follows:

$$K = \frac{P_u}{L \cdot D} \cdot \frac{(i + 1)}{i}$$

where
P_u = tangential force
L = pinion axial tooth length
D = pinion pitch circle diameter
i = gear speed ratio between pinion and wheel.

The K-factor is a practical relationship which is theoretically proportional to the square of the Hertzian pressure on the contact surface between the pinion and wheel teeth.

At the end of the Second World War, the big gear manufacturers in the U.S.A. (Westinghouse, General Electric, de Laval, Falk and Farrel-Birmingham) procured for themselves new, large and highly accurate gear-cutting machine tools with dividing wheels up to 5 metres diameter with twice as many teeth than had previously been used. New, accurate hobs were developed, and measuring instruments were introduced to check pitch errors and the accuracy of the involute tooth profiles. These new instruments showed that large errors occurred in the helix form if the temperature in the gear-cutting shop varied during the cutting operation. For this reason, temperature control was introduced, using air-conditioning equipment in the space surrounding the gear-cutting machine, such that the difference between day and night temperatures was no greater than about $\pm$ 0.5°C (1°F).

Against the background of these manufacturing advances, the General Electric announced in a 1950 development report (Reference 134) that sufficient knowledge and practical experience now existed to enable tooth-loading factors to be considerably raised. The report proposed the use of tempered low alloy nickel or chromium steel in the pinions.

By heat treatment, the hardness could be increased from 200 to 240 BHN[*] to 300 to 350 BHN. On the other hand, General Electric did not consider it advisable to give up carbon steel in the large gear wheel, which would be retained at 160 to 190 BHN.

The development envisaged the possibility of almost doubling the tooth loadings previously used for naval gears. Surface finish, extent of tooth contact and profile accuracy of the teeth were also successfully improved by a number of radically new machining methods. A

[*] BHN = Brinell Hardness Number.

1953 development report from General Electric (Reference 135) describes these important advances.

During the forties, the automobile and aero-industries had already started to finish-machine their highly-loaded gears by using special shaving tools. The shaving cutters had exceedingly accurate profiles with cutting serrations machined into the teeth, see fig. 31. The shaving was done by feeding the shaver into the gear wheel to be shaved. Because the shaving cutter does not have quite the same helix angle as the part it is shaving and is fed into the gear wheel with force, little shavings of gear material are removed. An exceedingly good surface finish is obtained in this way, and at the same time the hobbed tooth profiles are corrected to an accurate involute contour.

For small gears and small powers, improved load capacity with shaved gears was clearly established as well as a decided improvement in sound level. Through the initiative of the shaving wheel manufacturers, National Broach & Machine Co and Michigan Tool Co of Detroit, and the Bureau of Ships, a development program was started to introduce shaving for large marine gears as well. The Navy installed the first shaving machines at Westinghouse and General Electric, who developed the shaving method for wheel diameters up to 4 and 5 metres (160" to 200"). The American de Laval Company was not slow in following.

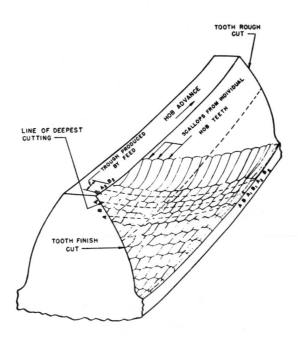

Fig. 30. Sketch showing in principle a hobbed tooth surface after the hobbing process.

When manufacturing a tooth by milling with a hobbing cutter, chip by chip from the tooth gap, a wave-shaped surface is generated, fig. 30. The differences in height between peak and valley are admittedly only about 3 to 7 micrometres after the finishing cut, using a quality hob. It is also very difficult to machine a perfect involute tooth profile all over the full pinion-wheel contact line. The thickness of the oil film under the Hertzian surface pressure occurring at the tooth contact surface is of about the same magnitude as the peak-to-valley distance clearances in the contact line for a hobbed tooth. Thus it is only the peaks that transmit the force. If the surface finish and involute errors can be improved, then the load on the teeth can be considerably increased. With a hobbed tooth surface, light metallic contact occurs between the surface peaks of the pinions and wheels. The oil film is penetrated and material can be destroyed locally by pitting or scoring. Flakes of metal loosen from the surface during pitting. Local welding of the pinion and wheel tooth surfaces occur during scuffing or scoring. The shaving process cuts these peaks away along the contact line, as shown by fig. 31.

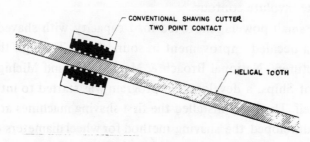

Fig. 31. The oblique shaving cutter machines the tooth flanks by means of the cutting-grooves in the teeth.

The shaving cutter, as portrayed by fig. 32, has an almost perfect involute form, and after machining, the gear teeth have a clearly improved tooth profile. A slight relief at the top and bottom of the teeth can also be shaved away. This relief is important for the formation of the oil film, and has been shown to improve the load-carrying capacity of the teeth. It is difficult to machine the teeth on the pinion and wheel so as to get a satisfactory contact along the entire tooth just by hobbing. By selective shaving, contacts of over 80 % of the tooth width can be achieved under load.

Fig. 32.

Appearance of
shaving cutter.

Fig. 33 shows a horizontal shaving machine with a single shaving head. Fig. 34 shows a vertical shaving operation for a large double helical gear wheel with two oblique shaving cutters, one for each helix. The shaving process spread at the beginning of the fifties to all the large gear manufacturers.

Fig. 33. Shaving one helix at a time in a horizontal shaving machine.

One experience with shaved gears was that the tooth surfaces were not damaged even under high local surface pressures, as occur, for example, with uneven contact between pinion and gear wheel. As long as hobbed gears were used, all that generally occurred was wear of the overloaded parts of the teeth, mostly in the form of pitting and scoring. In this way, the tooth loading was relieved over the length where the loading was greatest, with the result that the whole tooth length was more equally loaded, once the running-in period was over. This was why tooth failure was rare with gears that were only hobbed. On the other hand, wear of the tooth surfaces could be so severe that the oil film was destroyed. The improved surface finish provided by shaving permitted higher contact loading without risk of pitting. This encouraged the use of higher K-factors. Higher load levels on shaved teeth having local areas of overloading gave no warning of this condition by the traditional pitting evidence. Instead, the tooth fatigued and cracks occurred at the root. After a longer or shorter fatigue period, the tooth could break. A larger or smaller piece could thereby drop off and fall into the mesh with catastrophic consequences for the entire gear. The specific tooth loading (K-factor) had previously been the main criterion for hobbed gears. With shaved teeth and high K-factors, it was necessary to check also the bending stresses at the root of the teeth. Shaved and highly stressed gears therefore usually had larger and fewer teeth than those previously used.

Fig. 34.

Shaving two helices at
the same time in a vertical
shaving machine.

At the beginning of the fifties, the U.S. Navy introduced a method of raising the fatigue strength of teeth by shot-peening (initially developed by Joh. O. Almen of General Motors Corp). This was done after the hobbing had given the teeth best possible contact and tooth form. The resulting rough surface was unsatisfactory from a pitting resistance standpoint. Consequently, all gears were shot-peened first, and then finished by shaving to achieve satisfactory profile and surface finish. From tests carried out on rotating shafts, it was known that fatigue strength under bending stresses could be increased by cold-working the surfaces where the stresses were greatest. Cold-working was done by directing at high velocity a number of hard spherical steel particles against the surfaces to be worked. This produced high local compressive stress in the surface, while the material beneath the surface was subjected to mild tensile stresses. The result was that the surface layer was subject to lower tensile stresses under load and the fatigue strength could be raised by up to 30 per cent.

Accurate quality control methods, improved gear-cutting machines, shaving procedures and shot-peening, as introduced by the American gear manufacturers, gave the U.S. Navy a great lead over other navies for a long period. Tooth loadings for U.S. naval gears could be successively raised to around $K = 15$ and 20 bar (215 and 300 lb/in^2) for first reduction gears, and $K = 12$ and 19 bar (175 and 275 lb/in^2) for second reduction gears. The lower values were for aircraft carriers and heavy cruisers, while the upper values were for destroyers and frigates. During the sixties, warship gears were made with pinion hardnesses between 385 and 425 BHN*. Likewise the hardness of wheel rings was raised by replacing carbon steel by nickel or chromium alloy materials with 275 to 325 BHN. Pinions and wheels with this hardness could still be machined by hobbing and shaving.

The technique specially developed by NAVGRA in Great Britain using surface-hardened nitrided teeth with extremely high hardnesses, or case-hardened and ground teeth as developed by MAAG in Switzerland, has only slowly been adopted in the USA. There, the through-hardened material, with hardnesses allowing hobbing and shaving, has been largely retained, but on new warship units nitrided teeth have been gaining ground.

Steps in the development of marine turbine plant described here were carried out for the large aircraft carriers as well as for cruisers and the various types of destroyers and frigates.

Table 6.

Post-war development of U.S. aircraft carriers.

Launch year Deliv. year	Class Tonnage	No. of ships	Power/1000 kW	shp	Speed knots	No. of shafts	Mach. arr.	Steam cond. bar/°C lb/in²/°F
1954–58 1955–59	Saratoga 60000	4	209	280	34	4	GG[SP($\overline{HP+IP}$)+ LP] GE	84/510°C 1200/950°F
1960 1961–68	Kitty Hawk 61000	4	209	280	33	4	GG[SP($\overline{HP+IP}$)+ LP] W	84/510°C 1200/950°F
1960 1961	Enterprise 77000	1	209	280	35	4	GG(HP+LP) W. N.	49/sat 700/sat
1972–80 1975	Nimitz 83000	3	209	280	35	4	GG(HP+LP) W. GE. N.	49/sat 700/sat
1980–83 u.b.	Nimitz 88000	2	209	280	35	4	GG(HP+LP) W. N.	49/sat 700/sat

GE = General Electric   sat = saturated steam

W = Westinghouse   N = nuclear power

GG = Double reduction

GG(HP+LP) = cross-compound turbines with double reduction

GG[SP($\overline{HP+IP}$)+ LP] = cross-compound double reduction turbines with series-parallel connected high pressure and intermediate pressure turbines.

Table 6 lists the development of U.S. aircraft carrier machinery during recent years. According to sources available, powers have not increased since the 'Forrestal' class of the fifties, despite the fact that displacements have increased by nearly 40 per cent. Speeds too have been largely retained, 33 to 35 knots. The series-parallel arrangement with an integral high and intermediate pressure turbine means simple, compact plant with relatively good fuel economy at both cruising and full speeds.

The highest official power per shaft so far in operation is 52 250 kW (70 000 shp). From information received, however, short duration peak powers of $4 \times 56\,000$ kW (300 000 shp) have been developed by machinery of the 'Nimitz' class. With the 'Enterprise' a definite changeover to nuclear propulsion was made. She was thus given eight pressurised-water reactors of an enlarged submarine type. In the later classes these have been replaced by two large

* BHN = Brinell Hardness Number.

reactors. Steam pressure in the secondary circuit is said to be between 40 to 50 bar (560 to 710 lb/in²) with no superheating. The turbines are of cross-compound arrangement with water-separators between the high and low pressure turbines.

Table 7.

Post-war development of U.S. cruisers

Launch year Deliv. year	Class Tonnage	No. of ships	Power/1000 kW	Power/1000 shp	Speed knots	No. of shafts	Mach. arr.	Steam cond. bar/°C lb/in²/°F
1944—45 1967—69	Albany 17800	2	90	120	32	4	GG(HP+LP) GE	42/455°C 600/850°F
1959 1961	Long Beach 14400	1	59,7	80	30	2	GG(HP+LP) GE	49/sat 700/sat
1961—62 1962—64	Leahy 5760	9	63,4	85	34	2	GG[SP(HP+IP)+LP] GE DL AC	84/510°C 1200/950°F
1961 1962	Bainbridge 7700	1	44,7	60	32	2	GG(HP+LP) GE. N.	49 sat 700/sat
1963—65 1965—67	Belknap 6700	9	63,4	85	34	2	GG[SP(HP+IP)+LP] GE. DL.	84/510°C 1200/950°F
1964 1967	Tuxtun 8200	1	44,7	60	32	2	GG(HP+LP) GE. N.	49/sat 700/sat
1971—72 1974—75	California 9700	2 (+4)	44,7	60	32	2	GG(HP+LP) GE. N.	49/sat 700/sat
1974—78 1976—80	Virginia 10160	4	74,6	100	32	2	GG(HP+LP) GE. N.	49/sat 700/sat
1981—83 1983—84	Ticonderoga 9000	2 (+20)	59,7	80	30	2	4 GE LM 2500	CODAG—CP

GE = General Electric   W = Westinghouse   DL = De Laval   AC = Allis Chalmers
N = nuclear power   sat = saturated steam   GG(HP+LP) = cross-compound double reduction
GG[SP(HP+IP)+LP] = cross-compound double reduction turbines with series-parallel connected high pressure and intermediate pressure turbines
CODAG = Combined diesel and gas turbine
CP = Controllable-pitch propellers

Table 7 shows the development of U.S. cruiser machinery. The large cruisers of the 'Albany' class, built during the Second World War, were reconstructed during the sixties as missile cruisers. The power was 4×22400 kW (120000 shp) and the steam data was conservative at 42 bar, 455°C (600 lb/in², 850°F). The smaller 'Long Beach' class cruisers that followed were the first of their kind to get nuclear-powered turbines. The succeeding light cruisers of the 'Leahy' and 'Belknap' classes received more modern steam data of 84 bar, 510°C (1 200 in², 950°F) as well as series-parallel arranged turbines. After these ships were completed, nuclear propulsion became dominant and displacements increased back up to the 10 000 tons of the Washington Treaty.

Table 8 shows the growth of U.S. destroyers from the 1 000 tonners of the First World War and the 2 000 tonners of the Second. Speeds have remained between 30 to 34 knots. Steam data of 84 bar, 510°C (1 200 lb/in², 950°F) came first at the beginning of the fifties with the 'Mitscher' class.

Table 8.

Post-war development of U.S. destroyers and frigates.

Launch year Deliv. year	Class Tonnage	No. of ships	Power/1000 kW	shp	Speed knots	No. of shafts	Mach. arr.	Steam cond. bar/°C lb/in²/°F
1945—46 1945—46	DD Gearing 2425	45	44,7	60	35	2	GG[(HP+GCR)+LP)] GE W	42/455°C 600/850°F
1955—58 1955—59	DDG Forrest Sherman 2850	18	52,2	70	35	2	GG[(HP+GCR)+LP)] GE W	84/510°C 1200/950°F
1952—54 1953—54	DDG Mitscher 3675	4	59,7	80	35	2	GG[SP($\overline{HP+IP}$)+LP] GE W	84/510°C 1200/950°F
1958—60 1960—61	DLG Cootz 4700	10	63,4	85	34	2	GG[SP($\overline{HP+IP}$)+LP] AC DL	84/510°C 1200/950°F
1959—63 1960—64	DDG Adams 3370	23	44,7	70	31	2	GG[SP($\overline{HP+IP}$)+LP]	84/510°C 1200/950°F
1973—81 1975—83	DD Spruance 5830	31	59,7	80	33	2	4 GE LM 2500	COGAG—CP
1963—66 1964—68	FF Garcia 2620	10	26,1	35	27	1	GG(HP+LP) GE W	84/510°C 1200/950°F
1964—66 1969—73	FF Brook 2640	6	26,1	35	27	1	GG(HP+LP) W	84/510°C 1200/950°F
1966—73 1969—74	FF Knox 3011	46	26,1	35	27	1	GG(HP+LP) W	84/510°C 1200/950°F
1976—83 1977—84	FFG Perry 3605	74	30,6	41	29	1	2 GE LM 2500	COGAG—CP

GE = General Electric
W = Westinghouse
AC = Allis Chalmers
DL = De Laval
COGAG = combined gas turbine and gas turbine
CP = controllable-pitch propellers

GG[(HP+GCR)+LP)] = double reduction cross-compound turbine with geared cruising turbine

GG(HP+LP) = double reduction cross-compound turbine

GG[SP($\overline{HP+IP}$)+LP] = double reduction cross-compound turbine with series-parallel connected high pressure and intermediate pressure turbines.

The reasons for the rapid end of the epoch of steam after the 'Adams' class were the difficulties of ageing boilers and of getting trained crews during the sixties. The Secretary of the Navy decreed in 1967 that subsequent fossil-fueled destroyers should revert to the conservative steam data 42 bar, 455°C (600 lb/in², 850°F), the established standard of the forties and fifties.

This unsatisfactory state of affairs and the rapid development of gas turbine technology paved the way for jet engine-derived gas turbines to replace steam propulsion for larger fossil-fueled warships.

When the machinery was to be specified for the 'Spruance' class of 1970, the choice lay between gas turbine power, steam power and diesel power. The U.S. Navy, however, had very bad experience with their diesel-driven light escort vessels of the 'Claud Jeans' and 'Dealy' classes. A strategic comparison between the different alternatives left no doubt of the superiority of gas turbine installations. A COGAG* arrangement was chosen, where four General Electric LM 2 500 gas turbines were used. At cruising speeds, only two units were in operation, while all four were coupled to the two propeller shafts at full speed.

With gas turbine operation, considerable advantages were gained. Weights were low, manoeuvrability was clearly superior using CP propellers, and for overhauls only the jet unit was changed out and no work had to be done on board. Costs were lower, and the tactical advantages were superior.

By using C.P. propellers manoeuvring could be achieved without complicated astern gears and couplings. This type of propeller was developed to absorb the powers needed for the new gas turbine-driven destroyers, frigates and cruisers. The propulsive efficiency compared with fixed blade propellers was somewhat reduced but, in contrast to the Royal Navy, the American designers found that C.P.-propellers were of definite advantage, in that they permitted simpler and more reliable gears.

The only disadvantage for gas turbine operation was the necessity of using light, high quality fuel oils instead of the heavy fuels that could be burnt in steam ships. There is no sign at present, however, of the U.S. Navy returning to steam operation, even if the old advocates of steam power make themselves heard from time to time. It would seem, therefore, that the day of the fossil-fueled steam-driven warship is definitely at an end. Only nuclear-powered aircraft carriers, cruisers, destroyers and submarines remain as future niches for marine steam turbine manufacturers.

The development of frigates has followed a parallel course to that of destroyers, as shown in the lower part of Table 8. The last steam turbine-driven frigates were the forty-six 'Knox' vessels of 1963 with a power of 26 100 kW (35 000 shp) on a single shaft. When the 'Perry' frigates of 1973 came, the U.S. Fleet followed the path of the Soviet Navy and Royal Navy in adopting wholly gas turbine-powered ships.

* A COGAG = a machinery arrangement.(Combined Gas and Gas) where the gas turbines are used for both cruising and full powers. This contrasts with COGOG (Combined Gas or Gas) where special smaller gas turbines are used for cruising powers and uncoupled at full power.

3. TURBINE DEVELOPMENT IN THE ROYAL NAVY

3.1 The thirties and forties

The First World War ended with a clear victory for Great Britain and her allies. The British Fleet had victoriously fought a number of naval engagements aginst a German Fleet that was in many respects technically more advanced. Expansion of the Royal Navy during the war had been impressive but, in the following years, weariness with war and the hope for a peaceful future meant that only absolutely essential replacements for ships scrapped because of old age or obsolescence were approved. Great Britain was, however, still a great power and when rearmament commenced about 1935, there was much new construction to maintain her strategic position upon the seven seas.

Turbine designs in the great naval fleets of the First World War and during 1920s were very similar. Parsons Marine Steam Turbine Company played a dominant role as licenser of reaction turbines to both privately-owned and naval yards. Impulse turbines of largely similar designs were also being built under licence from Curtis in the USA, Zoelly in Switzerland and Rateau in France. For the manufacture of gearing, the specialist US companies held an undisputed lead in quality and design, although, the large yards, both in the USA and Great Britain, generally had their own gearing shops.

From the introduction of turbine propulsion in the Royal Navy, Parsons turbines had reigned supreme in the British Fleet until the famous Clydebank shipyard of John Brown acquired a Curtis licence and actively started to penetrate the marine turbine market. Their first success with the Admiralty came in 1911, when direct-drive Brown-Curtis impulse turbines were supplied to the first destroyer.

During 1913 and 1914, the Admiralty decided to try out these turbines in battleships and cruisers to compare them with Parsons reaction turbines. As well as being smaller and lighter, they proved to be more efficient, especially at cruising speeds. Nearly half the turbines installed in the British fleet during the First World War were of Brown-Curtis design.

At the outbreak of war, geared drive had only very recently come into production. Gear-manufacturing facilities were limited, which meant that, early in the war, the bulk of naval tonnage incorporated direct-drive turbines. The Parsons turbine, with its much greater number of rows of blades and larger blade diameters, had a more urgent need for geared drive than did the shorter, short-bladed Curtis turbine, in which the lack of gears was less objectionable.

Single reduction gears were adopted by Brown-Curtis as soon as they became available and their geared turbines were supplied in large numbers for destroyers, cruisers and battleships during the war. Their performance was so good that Brown-Curtis single reduction turbines were chosen for the battle cruiser, HMS Hood, with, for that period, the unbelievably high power of $4 \times 26\,900$ kW (144 000 shp).

As Brown-Curtis turbines developed, faster-running turbines with longer blades were installed. Some years after the war, when two new battleships were to be built (the Nelson and Rodney, delivered in 1927), the Admiralty again decided to fit geared Brown-Curtis turbines. This was regarded as an important milestone in favour of impulse turbines.

After a time, however, the Admiralty had to admit that the newly-built ships with geared Curtis impulse turbines were unreliable in operation. The turbines broke down more often than the Parsons units. Two elements in the designs especially caused trouble: blade failures occurred in both high- and low-pressure turbines. Cracks in, and failures of, the turbine discs were also recorded. These cases were similar to those suffered by the U.S. company, General Electric, during the great disc and blade flutter years of 1917 to 1920 (see Part I, p. 121). With the help of their brilliant scientist, Wilfred Campell, General Electric had overcome their difficulties in a surprisingly short time. Brown-Curtis, however, did not manage to master their problems in such a satisfactory way. On top of all these difficulties, Brown-Curtis did not have access to gear-cutting machines of the quality required by the gears for the high powers which were being installed. Their gears were noisy and suffered wear, and tooth failures occurred all too often. This unsatisfactory state of affairs caused such a setback to the reputation of Brown-Curtis turbines that the Admiralty excluded the company and their licensees as suppliers. In this way, impulse turbines disappeared from new-constructions in the Royal Navy during the 1930s and Parsons and their licensees became the only approved suppliers. Tables 9 to 11 depict the development of ships and machinery in the Royal Navy from the 1930s onward.

3.2 Destroyer development from the A-class to the 'Daring'

In general it was the destroyers — the ocean greyhounds — that were test beds for introducing new types of boilers and turbines. The large number of units in each class made it possible to use a ship in an existing batch for refitting and testing new designs without incurring excessive costs.

As shown in Table 9, destroyer boilers until 1950 had a relatively low steam pressure of 19 to 25 bar (260 to 350 lb/in^2) and superheat temperatures of up to 340°C (650°F). The good experience with higher steam conditions used in the U.S.A. and Germany, as well as pressure from Sir Charles Parsons, encouraged the Admiralty to equip the A-class destroyer, 'Acheron', delivered in 1930, with boilers and turbines designed for 39 bar, 400°C (550 lb/in^2, 750°F).

'Acheron's' turbine arrangement is shown in fig. 35. Live steam was admitted first to a geared reaction type cruising turbine (CRT) coupled to the intermediate pressure (IP) turbine rotor. Exhaust steam from the cruising turbine subsequently expanded successively in three turbines with separate geared rotors.

The high pressure (HP) turbine was of wholly reaction type, with no Curtis stage, and had a solid rotor with a dummy piston (fig. 36) The intermediate pressure (IP) turbine (fig. 37) was fitted with a built-on HP astern turbine with a triple Curtis wheel at its forward end. The low pressure (LP) turbine (fig. 38) had a drum type double-flow rotor. The forward LP drum had a single Curtis wheel, followed by a reaction section, for astern operation. The astern turbine in the LP turbine was connected in series with the astern wheel in the IP turbine.

In all Parsons marine turbines from 1920s, the shrouding was riveted to the reaction blades (fig. 39 and 40). There was large radial clearance between the stationary and moving parts. Sealing between stages was achieved by adjusting the axial clearance between the shrouding of the moving and stationary blades to a minimum value derived from tests. This was done by adjusting the axial position of the thrust bearing. The shrouding was divided into segments, each arc containing a group of from seven to twelve blades. One or more lacing wires

Table 9.

Development of destroyer turbines in the Royal Navy 1929 – 1978.

Launch year Deliv. year	Class Tonnage	No. of ships	Power/1000		Speed knots	No. of shafts	Mach. arr.	Steam cond. bar/°C lb/in²/°F
			kW	shp				
1929–34	A-D-E-F 1350-D	48	25.4	34	36	2	G(HP+LP) Pa BC	19–23/300°C 260/320/575°F
1930	Acheron 1350-D	1	25.4	34	36	2	G(HP+ IP+GCR+LP) Pa	39/400°C 550/750°F
1936–37	G-H-I 1300-1500-D	26	25.4/28.4	34/38	36	2	G(HP+IP+LP) Pa	25/340°C 350/650°F
1937–42	Tribal K-N-O-P 1700-1870-D	59	30/33	40/44	36	2	G(HP+LP) Pa	25/340°C 350/650°F
1940–44	L-Z-C 1700-1900-D	92	30/36	40/48	35–36	2	G(HP+LP) Pa	25/340°C 350/650°F
1943–46	Battle 2400-D	24	37.3	50	35	2	G(HP+LP) Pa	25/340°C 350/650°F
1950–52	Daring 1930-D	8	40.8	54	34	2	GG(HP+LP) EE	39/440°C 550/825°F
1954–59 1956–61	Whitby Rothesay 2380-F	11	22.4	30	31	2	GG(HLP+GCR) EE	39/440°C 550/825°F
1959–62 1961–64	Tribal 2300-F	7	15	12,5 +7,5	30	1	GG(HLP) MV G6	39/440°C 550/825°F COSAG-FP
1962–68 1963–72	Leander 2450-F	26	22.4	30	30	2	GG(HLP) EE	39/440°C 550/825°F
1961–67 1963–70	County 5440-D	8	44.7	30 +30	32,5	2	GG(HP+LP) EE+2 G6	46/510°C 650/950°F COSAG-FP
1971 1974–78	Amazon 2750-F	8	41.8	56	32	2	2 Olympus 2 Tyne Rolls Royce	COGAG-CP
1971 1975–78	Sheffield 3150-D	10	43.2	58	30	2	2 Olympus 2 Tyne Rolls Royce	COGAG-CP

Pa = Parsons   BC = Brown Curtis   EE = English Electric   MV = Metrovick

G(HP+IP+LP) = Three cylinder turbine with single reduction

G(HP+IP+GCR+LP) = Three cylinder turbine with single reduction and geared
cruising turbine coupled to intermediate pressure turbine.

G(HP+LP) = Single reduction cross-compound turbine

GG(HLP) = Double reduction single casing turbine

GG(HLP+GCR) = Double reduction single casing turbine with triple reduction cruising turbine

FP = Fixed-pitch propeller

CP = Controllable-pitch propeller

F = Frigate   D = Destroyer   G6 = Metrovic gas turbine

COSAG = Combined steam and gas   COGAG = 'Gas and gas' turbines

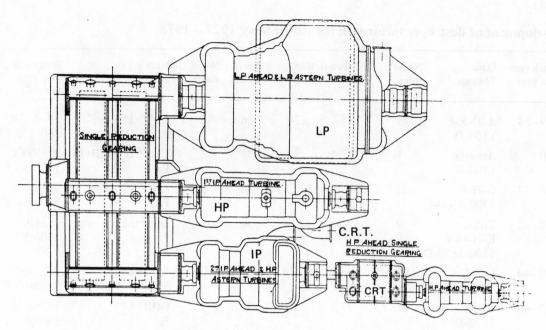

Fig. 35. Turbine arrangement in the destroyer, Acheron, 1930.
Power, $2 \times 12\,700$ kW (34 000 shp), 39 bar, 400°C (550 lb/in², 750°F).

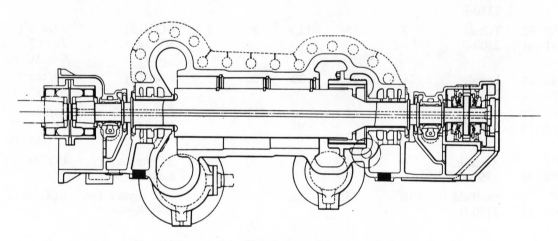

Fig. 36. Asheron's HP turbine, 3600 rev/min, solid rotor.

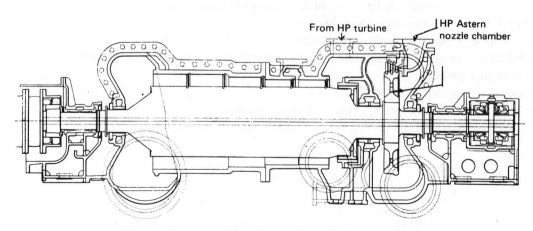

Fig. 37. Acheron's IP turbine, 2000 rev/min, solid rotor.
Triple Curtis stage astern turbine.

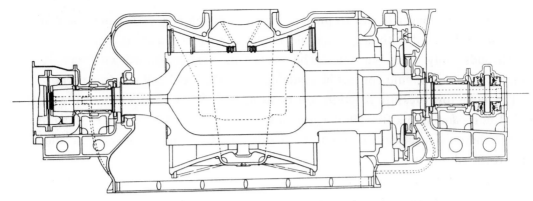

Fig. 38. Acheron's LP turbine, 1800 rev/min, drum-type rotor, double steam flow, Curtis LP astern turbine.

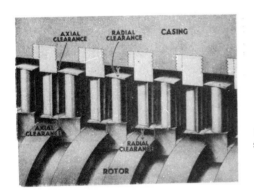

Fig. 39. High pressure blading with shrouding and axial seals at the tip and guide-vane shrouding.

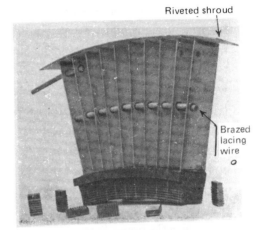

Fig. 40. Low pressure blading with shrouding and brazed-in lacing wire. Blade group with 10 blades.

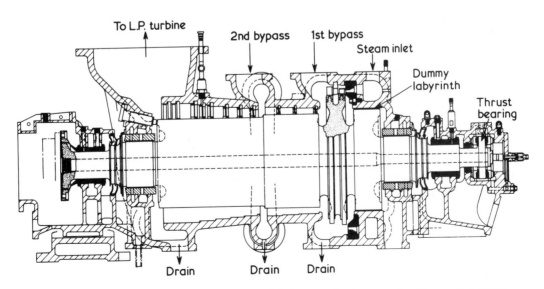

Fig. 41. Pametrada's HP turbine for 'Daring'. Solid rotor. Curtis stage plus 25 reaction stages.

were brazed to longer blades to prevent blade vibration (fig. 40). Land-based reaction turbines were designed with large axial clearances and small radial clearances: the blading had no shrouds, only brazed-in wires. The blade tips were machined with very sharp edges to minimize damage should contact be made between the fixed and rotating parts.

The large low pressure reaction rotors, as in fig. 38, were attached to the shaft ends by radial bolts and shrink fits. These rotors proved so sensitive to changes in steam temperature that 'Acheron's' machinery could never be operated without risk of sporadic and violent turbine rotor vibration.

After the totally unsuccessful 'Acheron' trials, the Admiralty reverted to their conventional steam conditions of 19 to 25 bar (260 to 350 lb/in^2) and 300 to 345°C (575 to 650°F). When rearmament commenced in 1935, however, construction was based on designs of 1930, scaled up to meet progressively higher powers. These British destroyers of the inter-war period had moderate powers and speeds compared with the French and Italian super-destroyers, which had speeds up to 40 knots and more. When war came, Great Britain had to produce and commission as many ocean-going men-of-war as possible. There was no time for new designs and testing. During joint operations with the U.S. Navy, however, the Adralty found that the U.S. ships were greatly superior in reliability and fuel economy.

At that time, the U.S. turbine manufacturers were employing pressures and temperatures well above British practice. An arrangement of double reduction impulse turbines with triple reduction cruising turbines (steam conditions 42 bar, 455°C, (600 lb/in^2, 850°F)), together with the high rotor speeds, had been fully tested in the USA since the 'Mahan' class of 1933. The Admiralty therefore decided, even before the war had ended, that turbines other than Parsons were to be tried out. Funds were put aside for the new 'Daring' class of destroyer. The machinery was to be built in collaboration with the leading turbine companies and to undergo comprehensive testing at Pametrada's large boiler and turbine test facilities at Newcastle-upon-Tyne.

Pametrada — Parsons and Marine Engineering Turbine Research and Development Association — was an organization formed in 1944 by Parsons Marine Turbine Co. and C.A. Parsons & Co., together with leading British licensee shipyards, as well as the land turbine manufacturers, English Electric, British Thomson–Houston and Metropolitan Vickers. Their intention was to concentrate design and development work, modernize existing turbine and gear designs and try out new types of machinery.

By 1945, the Admiralty had completed their preliminary studies for the new 'Daring' class destroyer. This was to be about the same size as the 'Battle' class built during the war but would have a higher power of 2×20 150 kW (54 000 shp). After detailed analysis, the Admiralty specified nominal boiler conditions of 42 bar, 455åC (600 lb/in^2, 850°F). Design contracts were placed for three different types of machinery (Mark I, II and III) with a cross-compound arrangement and double reduction gearing. The speed specified was 5 400 rev/min for the HP turbines and 4 500 rev/min for the LP turbines. Pametrada was commissioned to design the best possible reaction turbines for the Mark I design; British Thomson Houston was commissioned to design and build an HP turbine of the impulse type for Mark II design; English Electric was commissioned to design both HP and LP turbines for the Mark III.

Of the eight 'Daring' class destroyers, six were fitted with Pametrada turbines, one of these having an arrangement of British Thomson Houston's HP turbine and the Pametrada LP turbine. The remaining vessels were built by Yarrow and equipped with English Electric HP and LP impulse turbines.

The requirements for high r.p.m., steam pressures and superheat temperatures meant that Pametrada had to depart from the classic Parsons design in many details. The HP turbine (fig. 41) had a solid rotor, with a Curtis wheel impulse stage and 25 reaction stages. The reaction blades were arranged in groups with equal blade lengths but with more groups than in previous Parsons designs. Pametrada apparently still considered that a conical turbine casing, which would have allowed successively increasing blade lengths, was unnecessarily expensive to manufacture, despite such arrangements having been used for more than 15 years in U.S. and Continental-based reaction turbines. Four cast-in nozzle groups and two bypass valves both in the upper casing, were used for part-load, full load and over-load, respectively. Pametrada's LP turbine (fig. 42) had inherited features from several U.S. designs. The rotor was solid-forged and symmetrical, with 2×9 reaction stages and two parallel Curtis stages for astern power. The astern casing was free of the LP outer casing. Welded plate construction was used to a large extent. The condenser hung from the heavy frame of the bottom casing. All the moving blades had shrouding riveted with cylindrical tenons and were arranged in groups.

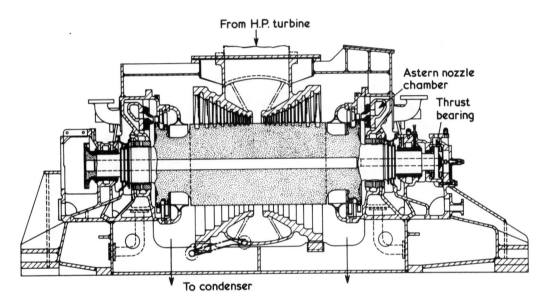

Fig. 42. Pametrada's LP turbine with 2×9 reaction stages.

English Electric's HP turbine (fig. 43) had one Curtis and eight impulse stages. The steam inlet chambers were cast into the top half casing as in the Pametrada turbine. The entire steam inlet chest, which was maintained at maximum steam temperature, must have been at odds with the cooler cylindrical turbine casing and probably caused some hogging during operation. An impulse turbine, however, can use quite large clearances between rotating and stationary parts. Furthermore, all glands were of the labyrinth type with spring-backed segments in both the diaphragms and shaft glands.

Even if the difference between Pametrada's HP and English Electric's HP impulse turbine was not so striking as that between the 'Farragut' and 'Mahan' turbines, the impulse design was definitely superior as far as dimensions and sensitivity to thermal gradients were concerned. Even so, the design lagged more than ten years behind General Electric in the U.S.A., who had already shown the way with small, compact, high speed, HP turbines.

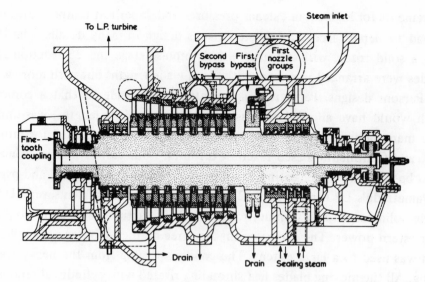

Fig. 43. English Electric's HP turbine with Curtis stage and eight impulse stages.

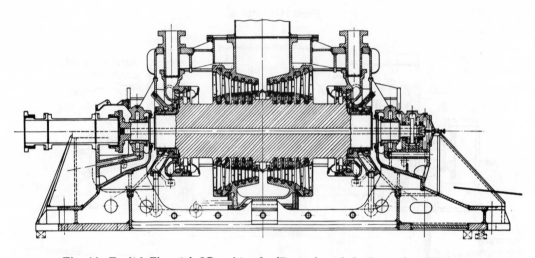

Fig. 44. English Electric's LP turbine for 'Daring', with 2×6 impulse stages.

The English Electric LP turbine (fig. 44) was, admittedly, shorter and lighter than Pametrada's but the difference was not as marked as in the HP turbine. The rotor had two blade groups, each of six impulse stages. The astern turbines were relatively free-standing with respect to the outer casing and the steam inlets were flexibly connected to the casings with piston-ring seals. This enabled the astern casing to expand freely when live steam was admitted during astern manoeuvring. Performance evaluation in the Daring class, showed that the English Electric turbines were superior to Pametrada's. Comparing the basic designs, this is hardly surprising.

In designing the Daring class, the Admiralty not only invested in new designs of turbines but also in double reduction gearing. Up to this time the Royal Navy had used single reduction gearing as previous attempts to utilize high turbine speeds with low propeller speeds by means of double reduction gearing had been unsatisfactory. Britain did not possess the accurate gear-cutting machines that were available in the U.S.. British gearing with double reduction had a reputation for being unreliable.

The machine tools used in the U.S.A. were also of quite another quality compared to those in the U.K. The Admiralty, therefore, had a second target for the 'Daring' destroyers, which was to produce gears of a quality that matched the best American gears. The Admiralty also wanted to specify the detailed requirements for accurate gear-cutting machines.

A group of experts was formed — the NAVGRA committee (*Na*vy and *V*ickers *G*ear *Re*search *A*ssociation) — with representatives from the leading British gear manufacturers together with Lloyd's Register of Shipping and metrologists from the National Physical Laboratory. The Admiralty produced fairly soon a standard specification for allowable accumulated pitch errors, tooth-to-tooth pitch errors and tooth surface finishes, as well as line contact lengths under load. By utilizing both British and foreign techniques and by collaborating with gearing manufacturers, great improvements in gearing quality were accomplished in a relatively short time. By these means, accumulated pitch errors could be reduced by a factor of ten relative to those previously regarded as acceptable for low speed, single reductions.

The shaving process was also introduced to improve tooth profiles and surface finish. The latter was thereby improved by a factor of at least two relative to that previously achieved by hobbing alone. Various pinion and wheel materials were investigated in laboratories, and different material combinations were tested in full scale trials.

A large number of tests were done to investigate various processes for achieving very hard tooth surfaces. The Swiss specialists, Maag of Zürich, who had a long experience of supplying case-carburised, hardened and ground gears, and who were the leading manufacturer of gear-grinding machines on the Continent, were called upon to provide a set of complete hardened and ground gears for a 'Daring' destroyer. The gears ordered for the 'Daring' class were all of the locked-train type with speeds of 5 400/4 500 rev/min for the turbines and 350 rev/min for the propellers. The basic design used traditional pinion and wheel materials with hobbed and shaved teeth. The pinion was made of low-alloy nickel steel and the wheel rims were of 0.4 per cent carbon steel.

Pinion hardness was 250 BHN* and the tooth loadings were chosen as K=7 bar (100 lb/in^2) for the first and K=9 bar (130 lb/in^2) for the second reduction. One set of gears was ordered, as already mentioned, from Maag who delivered case-hardened gears in the first and second reductions with hardnesses of the order of 500 VHN**, and a quenched and tempered gear wheel rim material in the second reduction of chromium-nickel steel with a hardness of 250 BHN. The tooth loadings of the Maag gears, however, were no higher than 18 bar (260 lb/in^2) for the first and 14 bar (200 lb/in^2) for the second reduction. Maag did not go to a higher tooth loading in the second reduction because they did not have access to a gear-grinding machine for gear wheels of the size required for the 'Daring' class.

Parallel with the introduction of Maag techniques for case- and flame-hardened gears, the NAVGRA committee initiated a comprehensive research project for developing nitrided gears. In this process, the finish-machined gear is placed in a retort filled with nitrogen. The nitrogen is absorbed into the surface layers after a certain time, forming nitrides which are very hard. The temperature required for this process is around 500°C (932°F).

Smaller gears could usually be taken directly from the nitriding retort without significant distortion or tooth surface damage. Their surface and accuracy were sufficient to be used

---

* Brinell Hardness Number.

** Vickers Hardness Number used for very hard materials.

without remachining. The NAVGRA group developed within a few years methods for nitriding quite large wheels without noticeable distortion. Some cases had to be touched up after nitriding to remove minor thermal distortions and the white layer which occurs during hardening in the nitriding retort. Nitriding steels with 3 per cent chromium and molybdenum could be nitrided to hardnesses of 700 to 800 VHN. Sufficiently thick nitride layers could be obtained with reasonable times in the retort.

3.3 Development of destroyers and frigates after 'Daring'

On the basis of NAVGRA's research, the Admiralty decided to increase pinion loadings for the smaller frigates of the 'Whitby' class delivered in 1956, thereby reducing the gearing dimensions and weight. 'Whitby' was fitted with machinery of $2 \times 11\,200$ kW (30 000 shp), and an English Electric single-casing main turbine with a speed of 6 200 rev/min and a declutchable cruising turbine. The gearing was made with hobbed and shaved teeth in through-hardened material of the traditional locked-train design with double helical gear tracks (herringbone teeth), as shown in fig. 45.

Pinion loads were more than double previously specified maximum K-values: $K = 16$ bar (230 lb/in^2) for first reduction and $K = 18.6$ bar (270 lb/in^2) for the second. The cruising turbine at lower speeds could be clutched-in by a self-synchronising coupling of the SSS-type. Experience with these high loads and non-hardened teeth was at first not completely satisfactory, mainly due to heavy pitting.

With the coming of the 'Tribal' class single-shaft frigates at the beginning of the sixties, it was found that the traditional steam machinery took up too much space and weight. The

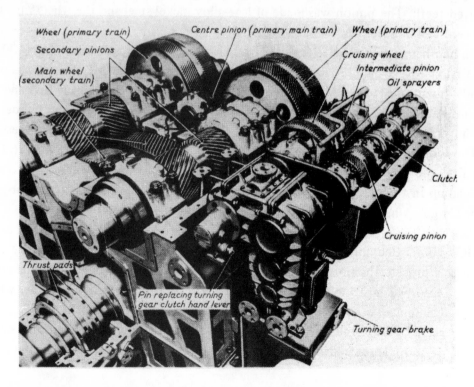

Fig. 45. The 'Whitby' frigate gear had hobbed and shaved teeth. Output 11 200 kW (15 000 shp).
One input pinion and a locked-train gear with a single-casing turbine for full speed.
Declutchable cruising turbine with extra gearing.

Admiralty decided to try out a COSAG* arrangement with a steam machinery of only 9 300 kW (12 500 shp) complemented by one Metrovick G6 gas turbine, of 5 600 kW (7 500 shp). Total power was therefore 15 000 kW (20 000 shp) on a single shaft. The turbines were designed by Metropolitan Vickers. This machinery, commissioned in 1961, was the first definite sign that the marine gas turbine era had started.

The gas turbines in the COSAG machinery were for use at top speeds and could be disconnected at lower powers. By providing the steam machinery with an astern turbine, moeuverability was assured and a normal fixed-pitch propeller could be used. To enable the ship to start rapidly without steam, the steam turbine could be manually disconnected, and the gas turbine connected by self-synchronising SSS clutches.

The 'Tribal' class gearing could never have been built to reasonable dimensions with pinion loadings from the 1940s. Pinion loadings of the 'Tribal' gears were K = 21.5 bar (312 lb/in²) for first reduction and K = 31.7 bar (460 lb/in²) for the second reduction.

In the large 'County' class COSAG destroyers with 2 × 22 400 kW (60 000 shp), not more than 50 % of the total power was provided by steam. The steam plant consisted of one cross-compound turbine combined with two Metropolitan Vickers G6 gas turbines on each shaft.

To get free choice of operating mode, the low pressure turbine had an astern turbine, and the gas turbines could also be used astern with hydraulic couplings and a reversing wheel. The gear was extremely complicated, as can be seen from fig. 46, with self-synchronising SSS clutches and hydraulic couplings for ahead and astern operation.

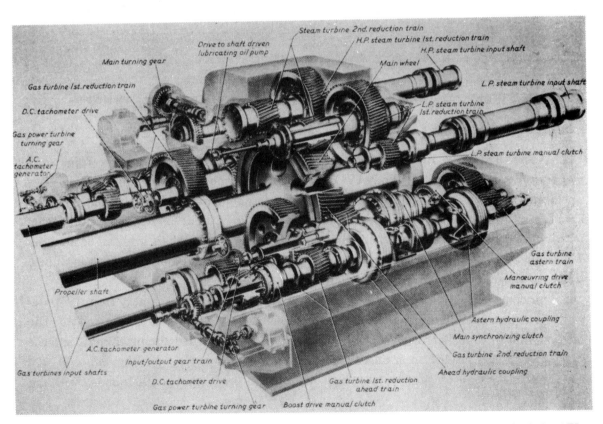

Fig. 46. The gearing of the 'County' class guided-missile destroyer with COSAG machinery built by AEI. Steam turbine output 11 200 kW (15 000 shp). Gas turbine output 2 × 5 600 kW (15 000 shp). The HP and LP turbines drove the propeller shafts through double reduction gears. The gas turbines were connected to the large gear wheel through self-synchronizing SSS clutches, intermediate shafts and hydraulic couplings for ahead and astern.

---

* COSAG = Combined Steam and Gas Turbines.

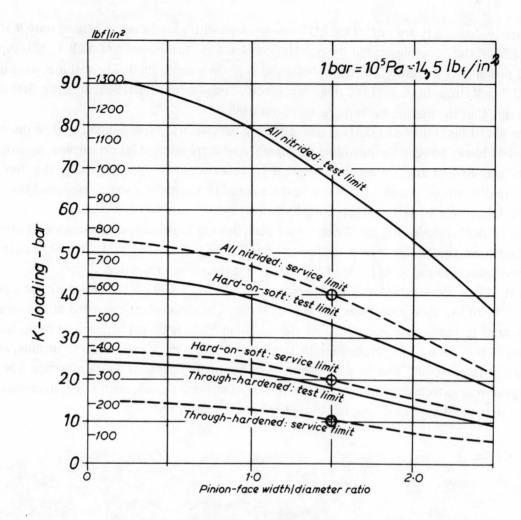

Fig. 47. Recommended tooth loadings from G.E.C. (U.K.) for various material combinations.

The development of British gearing technology is clearly shown in fig. 47, which summarizes an important part of the NAVGRA activities. Through-hardened and shaved gears operating at K-loadings of up to 10 bar (145 lb/in²); development of surface-hardened pinions against throuth-hardened wheels permitted a K-loading of 20 bar (290 lb/in²). For meshes with both elements surface-hardened, pinion loadings of 40 bar (580 lb/in²) can be allowed. This four-fold increase in just over ten years allowed a corresponding reduction in dimensions and weights.

Steam completely disappeared from new destroyer and frigate machinery from 1970 onwards, and an era of wholly gas turbine-driven COGAG and COGOG ships commenced. The introduction of propellers with controllable-pitch blades simplified the machinery, and the gearing no longer needed an arrangement for astern operation. As from the 'Amazon' and 'Sheffield' classes, steam propulsion, which started with the 'Viper' in 1901, ended with the 'Leander' in 1963.

3.4 Battleship machinery

In the British Fleet, as in other navies, destroyer machinery was the dominant field of development for new designs. For battleships, aircraft carriers and cruisers, development was more conservative in view of the enormous costs should a new design prove faulty. Improvements were made successively but the basic Parsons designs, with their drum construction, single reduction gearing and low turbine speeds lasted for a long time. It was not until after the Second World War that radical changes to battleship machinery were seen as an absolute necessity. Some classic turbine plants in the Royal Navy are described in this section.

There were only a few successors to the large number of battleships at sea during the First World War, as can be seen in Table 10. The 'Nelson' and 'Rodney' were designed for the newly developed 16-inch gun fitted in triple turrets. The weight of the armament resulted in a displacement of 33 300 tons, although the actual size of these ships was restricted by the International Washington Disarmament Treaty which was in force when the ships were being designed.

Table 10.

Development of battleship machinery in the Royal Navy, 1928 to 1946.

Launch year Deliv. year	Class Tonnage	No. of ships	Power/1000		Speed knots	No. of shafts	Mach. arr.	Steam cond. bar/$^\circ$C lb/in^2/$^\circ$F
			kW	shp				
1925 1927	Nelson 33300	2	33.6	45	23	2	G(HP+LP) BC	19/250°C 260/sat
1939–40 1940–42	King George V 36700	5	82.1	110	28	4	G(HP+CR+HP) Pa	29/340°C 400/650°F
(1939) –	(Lion) (40550)	(4)	97	130	30	4	G(HP+CR+LP) Pa	29/340°C 400/650°F
1944 1946	Vanguard 42500	1	97	130	30	4	G(HP+LP) Pa	29/340°C 400/650°F

G(HF+LP) = Single reduction cross-compound turbine

G(HP+CR+LP) = Single reduction cross-compound turbine with cruising turbine coupled
to high pressure turbine

BC = Brown-Curtis   Pa = Parsons   sat = saturated steam

This resulted in these ships being slightly smaller than the battle cruiser 'Hood'. Priority was given to armament at the expense of speed which was only 23 knots. The Nelson class machinery was similar to that of the 'Hood' but with two instead of four shafts and 60 % of the power, i.e. geared Brown-Curtis turbines, 2 × 16 800 kW (45 000 shp), steam pressure 19 bar (260 lb/in^2) with no superheat.

After the 'Nelson' class, there was a pause of almost 15 years before a new design of battleship was built. 'King George V' class was forced through just before and during the Second World War. The slow speed of the 'Nelson' class was regarded as a severe tactical drawback with regard to the risk from airborne bombs, and aerial and submarine torpedoes.

The 'King George V' and her four sister ships were thus fitted with four shafts and the much higher power of 4 × 20 500 kW (110 000 shp), giving a speed of 28 knots. For the choice of the turbine the poor reputation of Brown-Curtis proved decisive, and only Parsons was considered as a supplier for these ships. The Admiralty chose improved steam conditions: 29 bar, 340°C (400 lb/in², 650°F).

A cruising turbine was connected to the H.P. rotor via a declutchable dog coupling (fig. 48). A large diameter Curtis wheel was provided to give an acceptable peripheral speed at low powers but the reaction blades (15 stages) were extremely short, despite the large heat drop in the Curtis stage. In consequence, leakage losses were large and efficiency low; a poor arrangement in a turbine designed for economy. The rotor had a dummy piston and its own thrust bearing.

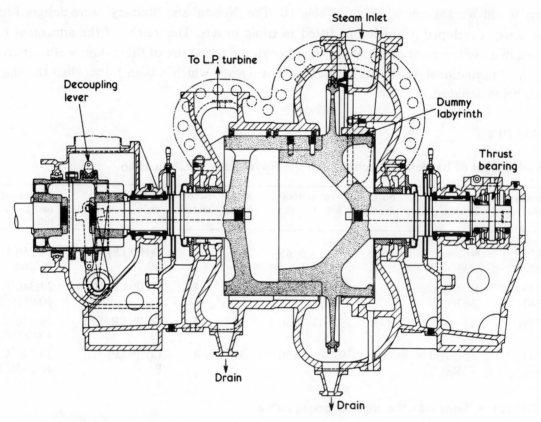

Fig. 48. The battleship 'King George V's cruising turbine connected to the high pressure turbine via a dog coupling. Speed at full power, 2 257 rev/min. Steam data, 29 bar 340°C (400 lb/in², 650°F).

The HP turbine, fig. 49, had the same low speed as the cruising turbine, turbine control nozzles were not fitted. The reaction drum had 35 blade stages in six groups with equal blade heights in each group. The rotor was a normal Parsons design with a drum fastened to the after shaft end by a shrink fit and radial bolts.

The LP turbine was, likewise, a traditional drum construction with double steam flow. The three-row Curtis astern wheel was placed at the forward end of the rotor (fig. 50). The HP turbine received steam from the cruising turbine at lower powers. For higher powers, it received live steam from the boilers via a valve which bypassed the first group. The gears were single reduction, with pinions for the HP and LP turbines respectively. The pinions had intermediate bearings and a relatively low tooth loading with K-factors below 6 bar (90 lb/in²). The gear casings were made of cast steel and very little welding was used. The bull wheel rims were bolted to the web plates. Propeller speed was 250 rev/min; the reduction ratio was 9 to 1.

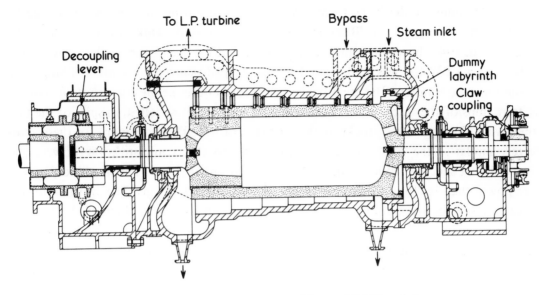

Fig. 49. HP turbine, 'King George V', speed 2 257 rev/min.

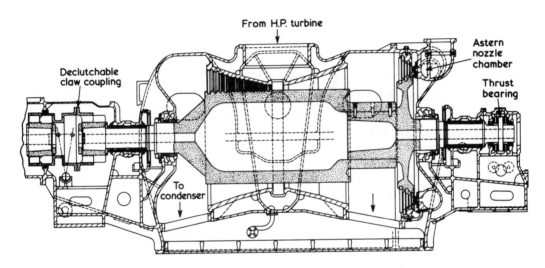

Fig. 50. LP turbine, 'King George V', speed 2257 rev/min.

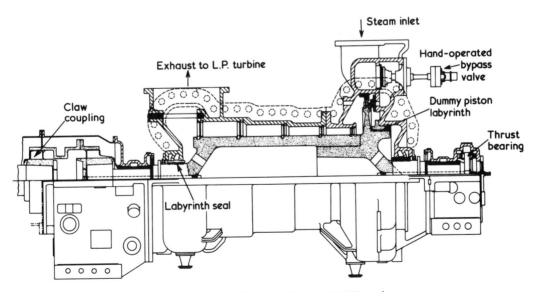

Fig. 51. HP turbine, 'Vanguard', speed 2 267 rev/min.

All five battleships of the 'King George V' class served during the war. King George V' took part in the sinking of the 'Bismarck' and her sister ship, 'Duke of York', sank the 'Scharnhorst'. In 1941, however, came definite proof that the age of the battleship was past, when the 'Prince of Wales' was sunk by a Japanese torpedo-carrying aircraft off Singapore during the Japanese invasion. The great behemoths proved quite helpless without air cover.

The four ships of the 'Lion' class, laid down in 1938, were cancelled, in spite of the fact that they were already on the stocks at the outbreak of war. The machinery for these ships was largely similar to the 'King George V' class. One ship, the 'Vanguard', was, however, so far advanced that she was launched in 1944 and fitted out in 1946. The machinery was of a higher power than in 'King George V', $4 \times 24\,300$ kW (130 000 shp). The cruising turbine was discarded and the HP turbine had a Curtis stage with nozzle control (fig. 51). The reaction drum was divided into four blade groups, each group having constant blade height. The LP turbine was almost identical with that of the 'King George V'. Both turbine rotors ran at $2\,267$ rev/min with a propeller speed of 230 rev/min. The 'Vanguard' was the climax of the battleship story in the Royal Navy. The era of the big guns and the giant battleships was over.

3.5 Aircraft Carrier machinery

Development of aircraft carrier machinery in the Royal Navy is shown in Table 11. The first carriers had already appeared at the end of the 1920s as rebuilt battlecruisers, since, by the Washington Treaty, there was no place for these large cruisers as originally conceived. So 'Furious', 'Courageous' and 'Glorious', of 22 500 tons, became the first aircraft carriers in the Royal Navy. They had adequate power and speed for use as aircraft carriers but suffered drawbacks because of the funnel arrangement, which, under unfavourable conditions, produced troublesome smoke from the boilers.

A long period of study preceded the building of the first aircraft carrier, designed as such, in the Royal Navy, the 'Ark Royal I'. This famous ship was ordered in the mid-1930s and was of about the same displacement as the previously rebuilt cruisers.

Power, however, was increased to 76 100 kW (102 000 shp) to attain the speed of 31 knots required for a floating "airfield". To split this power between two propeller shafts was considered impossible at that time, in view of the risk of propeller cavitation and the limitations of turbines and gears. The Admiralty decided instead to split the power between three propeller shafts, each of 25 400 kW (34 000 shp). The machinery was of the traditional cross-compound arrangement with low speed turbines having the same r.p.m. for both HP and LP cylinders. On the whole, the design was very similar to that of the battleship, 'King George V', built in 1939, but with greater unit power. The succeeding aircraft carriers were also fitted with similar Parsons machinery but the powers were gradually increased.

The two ships of the 'Eagle' class had a power of $4 \times 28\,300$ kW (152 000 shp) and a return was made to dividing the power among four shafts. Although the 'Eagle' class was delivered more than ten years later than 'King George V', Parsons had not brought about any major modernization of the turbines during this period.

Apart from the HP turbine (fig. 52) being furnished with separate nozzle chests bolted to the HP casing, the designs were unchanged. The arrangement of the five nozzle chests is shown in fig. 53. The chests were welded to flat plate covers which, in turn, were bolted to the turbine inlet-end casing. Two large base-load nozzle chests were arranged on the upper

Table 11.

Development of aircraft carrier machinery in the Royal Navy

Launch year Deliv. year	Class Tonnage	No. of ships	Power/1000 kW	shp	Speed knots	No. of shafts	Mach. arr.	Steam cond. bar/°C lb/in²/°F
1924 1928–30	Furious Courageous 22500	3	67.2	90	30	4	G(HP+LP) BC Pa	23/300°C 320/575°F
1937 1938	Ark Royal I 22000	1	76.1	102	31	3	G(HP+LP) Pa	29/340°C 400/650°F
1939–40 1941	Illustrious Indomitable 23000	4	82.8	111	30.5	3	G(HP+LP) Pa	29/340°C 400/650°F
1942 1944	Implacable 23450	2	110	148	32	4	G(HP+LP) Pa	29/340°C 400/650°F
1946–50 1951–55	Eagle Ark Royal II 36800	2	113	152	32	4	G(HP+LP) Pa	29/340°C 400/650°F
1942–45 1953–59	Colossus Majestic Centaur 13–18000	20	30–57 40–76		25–29	2	G(HP+LP) Pa	29/340°C 400/650°F
1953 1959	Hermes 23900	1	58.2	78	28	2	G(HP+LP) Pa	29/340°C 400/650°F
1971 1980	Invincible 16000	1	83.5	112	28	2	4 Olympus Rolls-Royce	COGAG–FP RG

G(HP+LP) = Single reduction cross-compound turbine

BC = Brown-Curtis   Pa = Parsons   FP = fixed-pitch propellers
RG = reversing gears

half of the turbine casing and three smaller ones in the bottom half. The large covers were necessary so that the nozzle chests could be taken out and refitted.

The Admiralty did not venture to use the usual Continental method of welding the nozzle chests directly onto the turbine casing. The LP turbine (fig. 54) was lighter due to the welded construction but the rotor designs, on the other hand, were unchanged. It is interesting to note that one row of guide vanes was placed in the astern turbine to change the flow direction of the exhaust steam when going astern. Thereby, the steam from the astern turbine was given the same rotation as the turbine rotor so preventing the exhaust steam from working its way into the aft portion of the ahead blading. This avoided the tendency to overheat that had earlier led the U.S. Navy to go in for twin astern turbines in their LP cylinders.

The smaller aircraft carriers of the 'Colossus' class had only two propellers and diverged little from the traditional Parsons design already described.

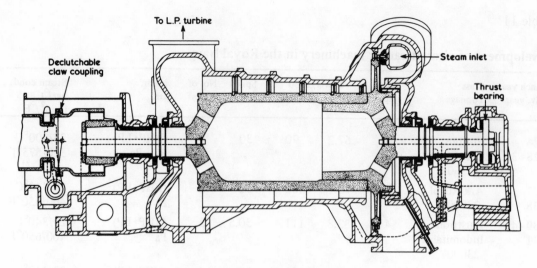

Fig. 52. HP turbine, 'Eagle'.

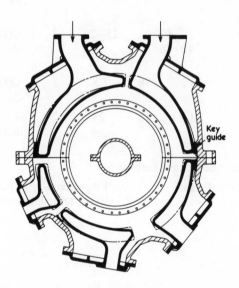

Fig. 53. Section through the nozzle chests in the HP turbine of the 'Eagle'.

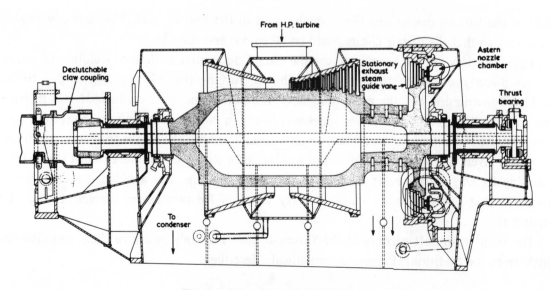

Fig. 54. LP turbine of the 'Eagle'.

It was with 'Invincible', delivered in 1980/81, that the new era for British aircraft carrier design began. The advent of STOL and VTOL (short and vertical take-off and landing, respectively) aircraft removed the necessity for the long flight deck. Displacement was reduced, partly due to the steam propulsion plant being replaced by COGAG gas turbine machinery, and partly because fewer aircraft were carried. Two marinized 'Olympus' jet engines with power turbines were coupled to each of the two fixed-pitch propellers via a reversing gearbox.

When 'Invincible' was being designed, the Western World had experience with c.p. propellers of up to 30 000 kW (40 210 shp) per shaft. The Soviet Navy had used c.p. propellers with even greater powers, but the Admiralty chose to develop a well-proven gearing design which, unlike a c.p. propeller, could be exhaustively tested in a test rig ashore under full load conditions.

The gearing had operated successfully at smaller powers in frigates and destroyers. A reversing gear does have the advantage of maintenance and repair without the necessity of dry docking. The result, however, is a large and exceedingly complicated gearing and coupling monstrosity. Fig. 55 shows the principle of the shafting, gearing and coupling arrangement for the power turbine of one of the four 'Olympus' units. Two such arrangements drive each shaft. With eight hydraulic couplings, four self-synchronizing SSS-clutches, 20 pinions and 25 shafts, the ship can be manoeuvred by any of the four units. From the power turbine to the propeller there is a triple reduction.

The power turbine of the 'Olympus' unit transmits its torque during normal operation to primary pinion X and primary wheel Y, to secondary pinion K and secondary wheel C and pinion R via the synchronizing SSS-type clutch. Pinion R meshes with the main wheel W which transmits its torque to the propeller. When manoeuvring, the SSS-clutch disconnects.

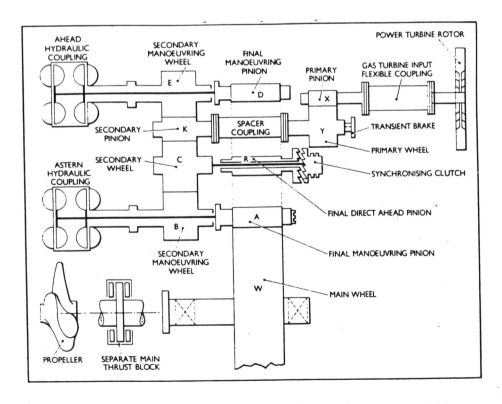

Fig. 55. Gearing and coupling arrangement of the aircraft carrier 'Invincible'.

Thus for ahead operation, pinion D is driven via K and E and the ahead hydraulic coupling which is filled with oil. For astern operation, the ahead hydraulic coupling is emptied and the astern is filled, thus transmitting the torque to the propeller via secondary wheels B and C to pinion A and main wheel W.

3.6 Development of cruiser machinery

At the end of the First World War, Great Britain had the largest fleet of battlecruisers in the world, but then their expense proved excessive in comparison to their strategic value and many ships of between 21 000 and 36 000 tons were either scrapped or sold during the thirties. However, two ships of the 'Renown' class, built in 1917, served throughout the Second World War; two ships of the 'Courageous' class of 1917 were converted to aircraft carriers. The 'Hood' was kept in solitary majesty until she was sunk in the World War II. Fifty-five light and medium cruisers with displacements of between 4 000 and 9 500 tons were largely "mothballed", although more than half were scrapped during the 1920s and 1930s. As a result of the Washington Treaty, a new class of cruiser was created, which joined the Royal Navy in considerable numbers from the beginning of the 1920s with displacements of between 8 800 and 9 900 tons; the seven units of the 'Kent' class of 1928 were the first vessels of this type. Machinery power was between $4 \times 13 500$ and $4 \times 15 000$ kW (72 000 to 80 000 shp). Brown-Curtis delivered a number of single reduction, cross-compound turbines to the 'Kent' cruisers, but they were not very satisfactory. Beginning with the four ships of the 'London' class (delivered in 1929) only Parsons turbines were thereafter fitted into British cruisers. Up to the end of the Second World War, 42 of these cruisers were built. As a cheaper version of these ships, 28 light cruisers with displacement of about 5 500 tons and powers between 45 000 and 54 000 kW (60 000 to 72 000 shp) were built during the same period, all with four shafts and Parsons single reduction, cross-compound turbines. Not until the late 1930s were boiler pressures raised to 29 bar (400 lb/in^2) and superheat to 340°C (650°F).

Only four cruisers have been completed since the end of the Second World War. Three ships of the 'Tiger' class (9 550 tons with automated steam propulsion) were laid down in the early 1940s and completed in 1959/60, two ships were then converted to helicopter cruisers. The fourth cruiser is HMS 'Bristol' (6 100 tons) which was completed in 1973 and is officially classified as a destroyer because of her lack of fire power.

'Bristol' is fitted with a combined steam and gas turbine (COSAG) plant of the 'County' type sufficient to give a speed of 30 knots.

The large destroyers and frigates of 'Sheffield' and 'Broadsword' classes have to a large extent taken over the strategic position previously held by the pre-war cruisers.

3.7 The end of the steam era in the Royal Navy

The Falklands War in 1982 once again proved the flexibility and reliability of steam plant in both Royal Navy and Merchant Navy ships operating under action conditions 8 000 miles from a repair base in appalling weather conditions for months at a time. Sadly, the new design of Type 23 frigate will have diesel-electric propulsion and there will be no requirement for any steam onboard this class of ship, in which even the evaporators will be heated by electricity. However, the Admiralty does not rule out the possibility of steam propulsion for future classes of ship, should the quality and availability of fuels for gas turbines and diesel engines deteriorate, or if the price should increase drastically.

Today steam propulsion is slowly disappearing from the surface fleet as the older ships are scrapped, and for a long time to come the Royal Navy will have to rely on its fleet of nuclear submarines to keep alive the art of steam propulsion.

The era of the steam turbine in surface ships started with the dramatic success of Parson's 'Turbinia' at Queen Victoria's Naval Review in 1897 and bowed out with equal success during the Falklands War, both events making headlines in the International Press.

4. THE DEVELOPMENT OF NAVAL TURBINES IN JAPAN

The wars of 1904–1905 and 1914–1918 had demonstrated Japan's tremendous need for warships if the ambitious Imperialistic objectives in Manchuria, China and the East Indies were to be realized. Almost a third of the National Budget of 1921 went to the Navy, of which one-half was for the new-construction of warships. The enforced allocations of the Washington Treaty of 1920 permitted Japan to extend her fleet to only 30 per cent of those of Great Britain and the United States. The Japanese military regarded this as an insult to the national honour.

In 1929 Japan invaded Manchuria and planned to strike southwards. The London Conference of 1930 allowed Japan to increase her cruiser fleet to 70 per cent of Great Britain's or that of the U.S.A. This permission was granted only after a strong threat by Japan to abandon the agreements. In 1936 Japan renounced both the Washington and London Treaties.

Japan built her first battleship in 1905, basing the engineering mainly upon British examples of that time, such as the battleship, 'Mikasa', Admiral Togo's flagship, built by Vickers around 1900. During the First World War, the British Admiralty and British engine builders gave the Japanese Fleet practically free access to Western technology. Britain even went so far as to design Japan's first aircraft carrier, the 'Hosho'.

From the middle of the twenties, Japan considered herself capable of standing on her own feet in regard to warship design. Great efforts were made in all branches of marine technology, but these did not preclude following all the new advances made by the navies of the Western Powers, buying licences where possible, or, quite simply, copying the designs. Thus, royalties were paid and maintained for licences held from Parsons and Brown-Curtis in Britain, as well as Zoelly in Switzerland, for keeping turbine designs for the Japanese Navy up to date. The licensing companies, however, were far from satisfied with these arrangements, as the Japanese were not willing to give any details of their operating experiences, nor any account of their own design developments.

The engine works of the large shipyards belonging to giant companies, such as Mitsubishi, Hitachi, Mitsui, Ishikawajima and Kure, designed their marine turbines on the basis of specifications from the Admiralty and were guided by the licensee material. In many cases, the Japanese designs must be regarded as superior to the original designs from the licensing companies. We shall not here go into any detail concerning Japanese turbine development. Only a few constructive solutions of their own will be noted, for both turbine and gear designs were generally fairly traditional. It can be observed, however, that Japanese designs used quite large safety factors, and for this reason their availability has to be judged as good.

With the end of hostilities in 1945, Japanese naval construction came to an abrupt end. Only a small number of designs will be described here to give a general view of Japanese technology as applied to naval turbines up till the end of the Second World War.

Fig. 56 shows an early, but very interesting, turbine design from the beginning of the twenties. The light cruisers of the 'Kuma' class had a standard displacement of 5 500 tons and a propulsion machinery of $4 \times 16\,700$ kW (90 000 shp). The turbines were single reduction, cross-compound arrangements. Propeller speed was 380 rev/min and the steam pressure was 19 bar (260 lb/in²) with no superheat. The Brown-Curtis origins are obvious, with shrunk-on discs in the high pressure turbine, whose speed was relatively high at approx. 2 800 rev/min. The low pressure turbine had double-flow and a single 3-row Curtis wheel for

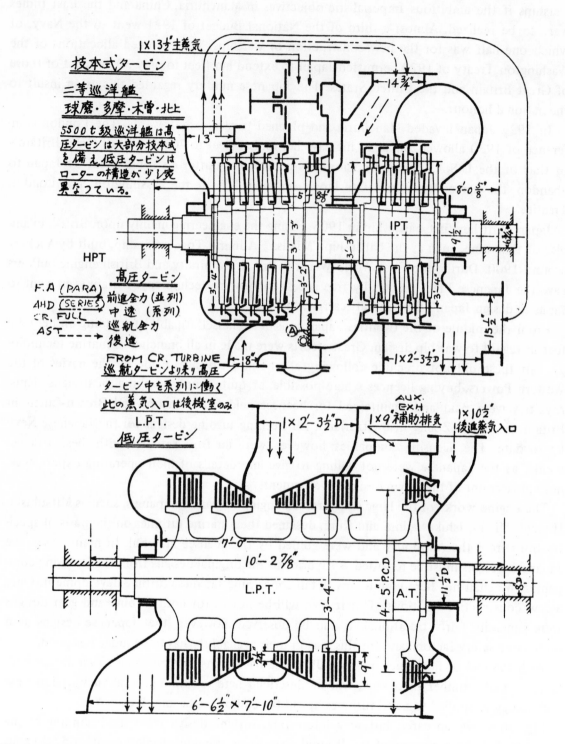

技本式タービン

二等巡洋艦
球磨・多摩・木曽・北上

5500t級巡洋艦は高
圧タービンは大部分技本式
を備え低圧タービンは
ローターの構造が少し異
異なつている。

HPT

F.A (PARA)
AHD (SERIES)
CR. FULL
AST -----

高圧タービン

前進全力 (並列)
中速 (系列)
巡航全力
後進

FROM CR. TURBINE
巡航タービンより来り高圧
タービン中を系列に働く
此の蒸気入口は後機室のみ

L.P.T.
低圧タービン

IPT

AUX.
EXH

1×10½
後進蒸気入口

L.P.T.

A.T.

Fig. 56. Main turbines of the cruiser 'Kuma', with the high and intermediate pressure turbines connected in a series-parallel arrangement. Built 1927. Power 4 × 16 700 kW (90 000 shp), 19 bar, (260 lb/in²) saturated steam.

astern operation. Speed was about 2 300 rev/min. Of paramount interest is the arrangement of the high pressure turbine, which had a built-in intermediate pressure blading section and utilized a series-parallel arrangement. At low speeds, in the series arrangement, exhaust steam from the high pressure blading could be led to the intermediate turbine and at high speeds, in the parallel arrangement, direct to the low pressure turbine. As far as the author has been able to ascertain, this is the first well-developed series-parallel design with only a single rotor for high and intermediate pressure blading. This design was twenty years earlier than Brown-Boveri's solution of the series-parallel connection. Blohm & Voss' single rotor design was also much later. The American series-parallel designs were no less than thirty years behind the 'Kuma' turbines.

Figs 57 and 58 show a much larger turbine installation with a geared cruising turbine for the 'Mogami' cruisers, completed from 1935 to 1937. Displacement was 8 500 tons, and the power 4×28 300 kW (152 000 shp). The speed was 37 knots, and the steam pressure was 19 bar (260 lb/in^2) with superheat to 285°C (545°F). The cruising turbine ran at approx. 5 000 rev/min and was uncoupled at full load. It is interesting to note how few impulse stages the Japanese designs utilized. Turbine speeds were relatively low, 2 600 rev/min for high and intermediate pressure turbines, and 2 300 rev/min for low pressure turbines. Propeller speed is said to have been 340 rev/min. Tooth loadings were moderate with a K-factor of 6.2 bar (90 lb/in^2). The astern turbine was a three-row Curtis wheel in the low pressure turbine. From what the author has learned, Japanese manufacturers of naval turbines used impulse turbines almost exclusively. Heavy turbine discs and moderate speeds were generally chosen. In this way, the blade and disc vibrations that were such a crippling weakness of Brown-Curtis turbines, were by and large avoided.

Fig. 59 shows a section through the turbines of the famous battleship 'Yamato'. This leviathan was delivered in 1941 with a standard displacement of 62 300 tons. Her power was 4×28 000 kW (150 000 shp). With such a large displacement the speed was only 27 knots. The contemporary U.S. battleships of the 'South Dakota' class can serve as a comparison. They had a power of 4×24 300 kW (130 000 shp) with a displacement of 38 000 tons and a speed of 28 knots. The 'Yamato' design with shrunk-on impulse discs was the same as that used ever since the 'Mogami' class cruisers, and was known as 'Kanpon-Shiki' (Japanese Navy Type).

Four cruising turbines were coupled to the high pressure turbine pinions as shown by fig. 60, not as for the 'Mogami' class coupled to the intermediate pressure turbines. To cope with the tooth loadings at the very low propeller speeds of 225 rev/min, the designers chose to make use of four pinions and double parallel low pressure turbines. The high pressure and intermediate pressure turbines were placed at the after end of the gearing. The low pressure turbines each had a triple Curtis astern wheel built into their free end. The steam pressure was 25 bar (350 lb/in^2) with 350°C (662°F) superheat. The turbine speeds were 3 300 rev/min for the high pressure turbines, and 2 140 rev/min for the low pressure turbines. The cruising turbines ran at 6 350 rev/min and operated up to a propeller speed of 130 rev/min, whereafter they were disconnected at higher powers. Tooth loadings in the gearing (according to the author's calculations) rose only to approx. 4.3 bar (62 lb/in^2). Although the designs, compared with corresponding U.S. battleship machinery, must be assessed as behind the times in the areas of weight and performance, they proved to be quite suited for their purpose and had a performance easily comparable to the corresponding European designs. The two battleships of the 'Yamato' class were enormous fighting machines and had a fantastic set of big guns, fig. 61. This did not, however, prevent both ships from being sunk by

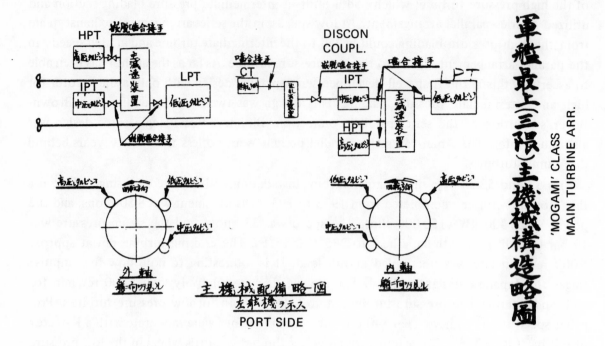

Fig. 57 & 58. Turbine arrangement of the heavy cruiser 'Mogami'. Power 4 × 28 500 kW (152 000 shp). Built 1935. Arrangement G(HP + GCR + IP + LP), geared cruising turbines on the inboard shafts, none on the outboard shafts. Steam data, 19 bar (260 lb/in²), 285°C (545°F).

Ⅱ 軍艦最上主機械計算実例

軍艦最上主機配備図

MAIN TURBINE ARRANGEMENT

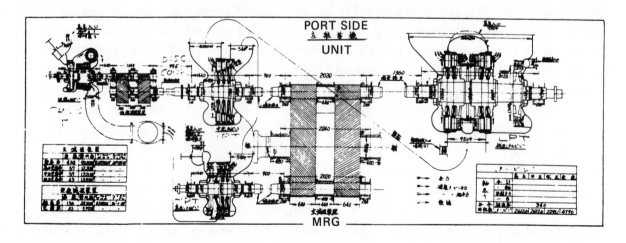

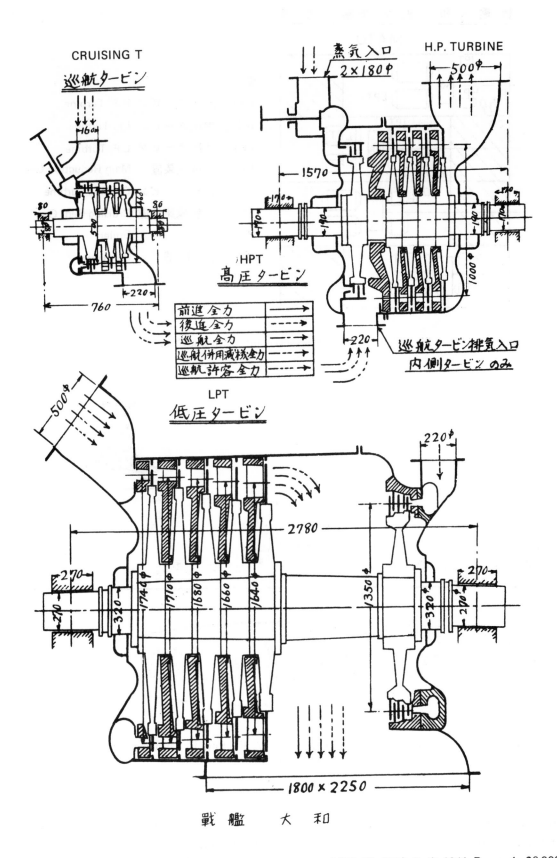

Fig. 59. Turbines of the battleship 'Yamato'. Arrangement G(HP+IP+2LP). Built 1941. Power 4 x 28 000 kW (150 000 shp). Steam data, 25 bar, 325°C (350 lb/in², 615°F).

76

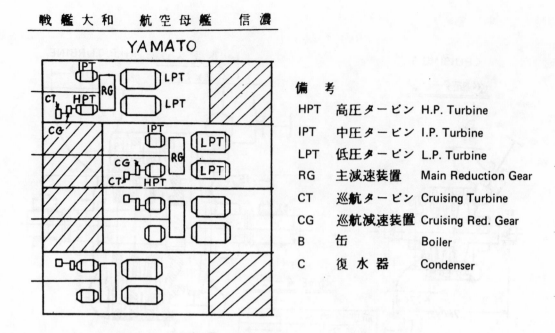

戦艦大和　航空母艦　信濃

YAMATO

備 考

HPT	高圧タービン	H.P. Turbine
IPT	中圧タービン	I.P. Turbine
LPT	低圧タービン	L.P. Turbine
RG	主減速装置	Main Reduction Gear
CT	巡航タービン	Cruising Turbine
CG	巡航減速装置	Cruising Red. Gear
B	缶	Boiler
C	復水器	Condenser

Fig. 60. Turbine room arrangement, battleship 'Yamato'.

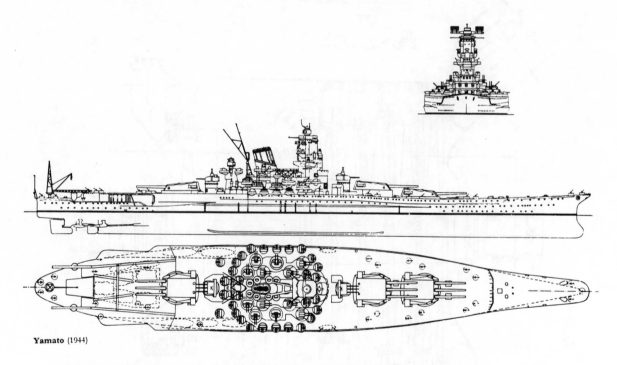

Yamato (1944)

Fig. 61. The battleship 'Yamato' in all her glory. 62 300 tons. Her armaments were nine 45 cm (17.7 ins) and twelve 16 cm (6.3 ins) guns.

American planes; but it did take about 10 torpedoes and 6 bombs to sink the 'Yamato', and about 19 torpedoes and 17 bombs to sink her sister, the 'Musashi'.

As already mentioned, the Japanese Fleet early abandoned Parsons designs and built turbines of the "Japanese Navy Type", which meant modified Brown-Curtis designs. The Japanese had very good contacts with the German Navy prior to the Second World War. The Germans got them interested in reaction type turbines. To gain experience with modern reaction turbines in a simple way, an order was placed with Brown Boveri of Baden for two double reduction units for a small special ship, 'Kashino', with an output of 2x2 200 kW (6 000 shp). In principle, Brown Boveri was allowed to choose the steam conditions and the design arrangement. The only requirements were that the units should be modern and have low weight and low steam consumption. The steam conditions were therefore high, 51 bar (725 lb/in²), 450°C (842°F). The order was placed in 1936, and the ship made her trials in 1941. This machinery, which was the first ever designed by the author, was quite special with hydraulic governing, welded low pressure rotors and single helical gears with thrust collars.

At the same time as the turbine order, the Japanese Navy ordered a Velox boiler suitable for building into the same ship. The Velox boiler, however, was never to operate at sea. It was erected first on land where it underwent thorough testing. The Japanese Navy found that the Velox design was far too complicated for sea duty. The 'Kashino', therefore, was furnished with two oil-fired boilers of a more normal type. The turbines had a cross-compound arrangement with double reduction gears, fig. 62.

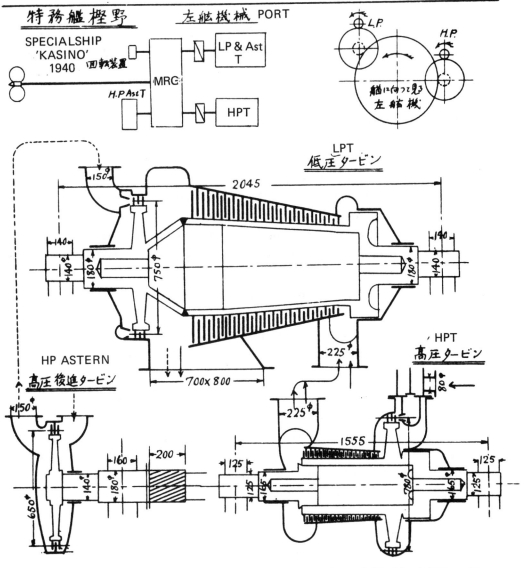

Fig. 62. Small, double reduction reaction turbine for a special vessel, 'Kashino', delivered by Brown Boveri in 1939. Power 2x2200 kW (6000 shp), 51 bar, 450°C (725 lb/in², 842°F). (Designed by the author.)

Figs 63 and 64.
High pressure manoeuvring gear of the 'Kashino', with three governing valves controlled by rotary pistons. Both units were manoeuvred from a central control platform with hydraulic actuators and all necessary instrumentation.

The high pressure turbine ran at 4 500 rev/min, and the low pressure turbine at 3 500 rev/min, and were geared down to a propeller speed of 160 rev/min. To provide the specified high astern power, both rotors were provided with astern blading consisting of a single Curtis wheel. The high pressure astern turbine was coupled to the high pressure turbine pinion and was an overhung wheel in a separate turbine casing. The astern turbine in the low pressure casing was of a similar type and connected steamwise in series with the high pressure astern turbine.

The reaction blading in both high and low pressure turbines had continuously increasing blade lengths. The high pressure rotor had a constant drum diameter and a conical casing. The low pressure turbine had both conical drum and conical casing. The low pressure drum consisted of two parts welded together, one of the first examples of a wholly welded rotor at Brown Boveri. This design, which was initiated by Brown Boveri's technical director, Dr Adolph Meyer, later proved a great advance. Nowadays, most large low pressure reaction type power station rotors are of welded construction.

The double reduction gearing was single helical in both reductions. Axial thrust was absorbed by a specially designed thrust collar developed by Brown Boveri. All manoeuvring valves were hydraulically actuated. The three nozzle valves of the ahead turbine, and the two of the astern turbine, were all moved by rotary pistons controlled by cam-operated valves, figs 63 and 64. The units were manoeuvred from a central control platform with hydraulic actuators to each of the rotary pistons. When the order was placed, the Japanese expressed a certain distrust of the high temperatures. Brown Boveri were compelled to guarantee that in an emergency the turbine units could be started up from cold to full speed in five minutes.

This manoeuvre was demonstrated on each unit on the test bed by simulating the ship's operating conditions as far as possible and by the use of a large water brake. The starting trials were performed without difficulty. The normal starting time from cold to full power was half an hour, and this extreme emergency start was not allowed to be carried out more than once a year.

To sum up, it must be said that Japanese technicians and yards made a great contribution to the expansion of their naval fleet before World War II came to its bitter end. The entire fleet was, in fact, already largely destroyed before capitulation. Japan has since then been extremely unwilling to start again, and only after pressure has begun to build a naval defence force. A smaller number of frigates of U.S.-influenced designs have appeared. On the other hand, Japanese ship construction has gained a leading world position for the production of merchant shipping, in regard to both quality and quantity.

5. NAVAL TURBINE MANUFACTURERS IN CONTINENTAL EUROPE

5.1 The large turbine firms

The successes of the two Parsons companies on land and at sea persuaded the numerous European manufacturers of steam engines to acquire licences at an early stage. Thus, the Swiss Company of Brown Boveri & Cie signed a licence agreement in 1901 for land-based turbines that also covered their subsidiaries in France and Germany. The German Navy, which was undergoing rapid development, decided in 1903 to build turbine-driven destroyers and cruisers in order to try out the new type of machinery. A holding company was formed, "Turbinia-Brown Boveri-Blohm & Voss", to exploit the Parsons patents and "know how". "Turbinia" granted licences to other shipyards than Blohm & Voss, and the group soon became the main contractor to the German Fleet. In a short while, Brown Boveri of Mannheim became a large supplier of naval turbines.

Besides the Parsons group, the large German electrical firm Allgemeine Elektrische Gesellschaft (AEG) in Berlin soon entered the scene with a Curtis licence. AEG also collaborated with several shipyards, among them Dr Gustaf Bauer's famous Vulkan Werft in Hamburg. This firm had built the machinery for the largest Atlantic liner of that time, the 'Imperator'. Blohm & Voss had built the somewhat earlier 'Vaterland', another famous Atlantic liner equipped with Parsons turbines. Competition between suppliers of reaction and impulse turbines was extremely lively, and each side claimed superiority over the other.

When the demand for geared marine turbines grew, Brown Boveri, AEG and several yards acquired large gear works equipped with excellent gear-cutting machinery for those days. Zoelly in Switzerland granted a licence for their impulse turbine designs to the large companies of MAN in Germany and Schneider in France. The Companie Electro-mechanique (CEM) in France had access to Parsons licences through their parent company, Brown Boveri, as well as the use of Brown Boveri's own designs. Rateau impulse turbines appeared in 1900 with machinery ordered by the French Navy for a small torpedo boat of 750 kW (1 000 shp). Rateau subsequently built up a leading position as supplier and licensing company to French shipyards. In a while, Rateau designs took the lion's share of orders for destroyer turbines. CEM, however, installed reaction turbines in several of the larger French warships. Schneider and Zoelly turbines were also installed in a number of lighter ships.

The Italian Navy, which prior to Mussolini had been relatively insignificant, experienced a rapid rise during the thirties. The turbine firm, Franco Tosi, and the large shipyards in Genoa, La Specia and Trieste signed licence agreements with Parsons. Impulse turbines were also built, although to a lesser degree. Cantieri del Tirreno and Beluzzo made turbines based on Curtis licences.

5.2 Germany — Inter-War and Second World War

The very considerable naval fleet built up by Germany before the First World War was destroyed or fell into the hands of the victorious powers. Only a few, almost antique, ships remained in the German Navy when that country planned to rebuild their fleet in the beginning of the thirties. When Hitler came to power, an intensive expansion began, which in the beginning was admittedly limited by the Armistice agreement and the Washington and London Treaties.

Because of Hitler's strong conviction that aircraft and submarines could win a war against Great Britain, there was no consistent construction of surface vessels, but a number of interesting units were, however, built. In 1935 Germany was given permission by the victorious powers to build up her naval fleet to a maximum of 35 per cent of that of Great Britain. In 1938, however, Hitler renounced all current naval agreements. Table 12 shows how the German naval engineers attempted to develop various solutions for propulsion machinery for surface vessels, which, in retrospect, must be regarded as rather inconsequent.

Table 12.

Rebuilding of the German Navy, 1930 to 1945.

Deliv. year	Class Tonnage	No. of ships	Power/1000 kW	shp	No. of shafts Speed, knots	Mach. arr. Manufacturer	Steam cond. bar/$^\circ$C lb/in^2/$^\circ$F
1938–39 BS	Scharnhorst Gneisenau	2	121	165	3 32	G(HP+IP1+IP2+LP) BBC Deschimag	60/450°C 855/840°F
1940 BC	Bismarck 41700	1	101	138	3 30	G(HP+IP+LP) B. & V.	60/450°C 855/840°F
1941 BS	Tirpitz 42900	1	101	138	3 30	G(HP+IP1+IP2+LP) BBC	60/450°C 855/840°F
1925 C	Emden 5600	1	34	45.9	2 29.5	G(HP+LP) BBC	25/300°C 350/570°F
1929–30 C	Königsberg	3	47.8	65	2 32	2G(HP+LP)+ 2 MAN-diesel COSOD	32/350°C 450/660°F
1931 C	Leipzig 6515	1	44	60	3 31	2G(HP+LP) 1×4 MAN-diesel COSAD	32/350°C 450/660°F
1935 C	Nürnberg 6250	1	44	60	3 32	G(HP+LP)	32/350°C 450/660°F
1933–36 C	Deutschland 11700	3	40	54	2 28	2×4 MAN-diesel	4-cycle geared double-acting
1939–40 C	Hipper 14–17000	4	97	132	2 32.5	G(CR+HP+IP+LP) BBC Deschimag	71/450°C 1015/840°F
1936 D	Z1-8 1625	8	51.5	70	2 38	G($\overline{GCR+HP}$+IP+LP) Deschimag	76/450°C 1115/840°F
1937–38 D	Z9-16 1625	8	51.5	70	2 38	G($\overline{HP+LP}$+$\overline{IP+LP}$) Blohm & Voss	125/450°C 1800/840°F
1938–39 D	Z17-22 1811	6	51.5	70	2 40	G[SP($\overline{HP+IP}$)+LP] Deschimag	73/450°C 1045/840°F
1940–41 D	Z23-30 2605	8	51.5	70	2 38.5	G[SP($\overline{HP+IP}$)+LP] Deschimag	73/450°C 1045/840°F
1942–43 D	Z31-39 2603	7	51.5	70	2 38.5	G[SP($\overline{HP+IP}$)+LP] Deschimag	73/450°C 1045/840°F
1943–44 D	Z35-45 2527	5	51.5	70	2 38	G[SP($\overline{HP+IP}$)+LP] Deschimag	73/450°C 1045/840°F

BS = Battleship
BC = Battlecruiser
C = Cruiser
D = Destroyer
SP = Series/parallel arrangement

COSOD = Combined steam or diesel machinery
COSAD = Combined steam and diesel machinery

For the 'Emden' class cruisers of 1925, traditional steam machinery was chosen of $2 \times 17\,000$ kW (45 900 shp). When the 'Königsberg' class was built, German naval designers were ready, for the first time in history, to try out large diesel engines for a cruiser, although only for cruising speeds. Two MAN diesel engines were coupled to the propeller shafts and gave the ship a cruising speed of 10 knots with this early COSOD machinery (Combined Steam or Diesel). In the 'Leipzig' class of 1931, a COSAD (Combined Steam and Diesel) arrangement was tried in a more consistent manner. With four large diesel engines on the centre shaft, a very economic propulsion plant was obtained, well adapted to a war against enemy merchant fleets that the Germans early planned.

The 'Deutschland' class appeared in 1933. According to the Washington Treaty, these ships were not to have a greater standard displacement than 10 000 tons, but were actually made almost 20 per cent larger. Four diesel engines were installed on each of the propeller shafts, and the power obtainable was $2 \times 20\,000$ kW (54 000 shp).

Experience with the MAN diesels, however was not entirely satisfactory, and for the 'Hipper' class cruisers that were built just before the outbreak of war, a return was made to steam power. The steam pressure for the 'Hipper' ships was a radical 71 bar (1015 lb/in^2) with 450°C (842°F) superheat. With the battle cruisers 'Scharnhorst' and 'Gneisenau', delivered during 1938 and 1939, the Germans considered that they had created worthy opponents to the British battleships and battle cruisers. Their power was $3 \times 40\,300$ kW (165 000 shp). The main turbines, which had a very high unit output for their day, were designed by Brown Boveri of Mannheim with four pinions and four turbine rotors. The steam expanded through a high pressure turbine, two intermediate pressure turbines and finally a double-flow low pressure turbine, see fig. 65.

These units had an arrangement with bypass valves on both the high pressure and first intermediate pressure turbines. At higher powers, live steam was admitted directly to the Curtis wheel of the first intermediate pressure turbine. To produce sufficient astern power, two pinions had to be utilized, and astern turbines were installed in both the second intermediate pressure turbine and the low pressure turbine. The astern blading in the low pressure turbine had an unusual position in the centre of the rotor. The direction of the ahead steam flow was from the ends of the turbine towards the centre. Exhaust steam from the second intermediate turbine was led through enormous pipe connections over to the low pressure turbine. The three propeller shafts could operate quite independently and be disconnected from the gearing. The uncoupled propellers could then rotate freely and thereby radically reduce the drag resistance from the propeller.

The 'Tirpitz' machinery was likewise delivered by Brown Boveri of Mannheim. It had a somewhat lower power than the 'Scharnhorst', but otherwise did not deviate very much. The propeller speed was 260 rev/min against 280 rev/min for the 'Scharnhorst'. The main machinery of the 'Bismarck', fig. 66, was built by Blohm & Voss and was also a typical reaction design, although rather differently arranged to Brown Boveri's.

The turbine speeds were considerably lower, and only three rotors were used. The high pressure turbine had six separate hand-controlled nozzle valves, but only one bypass valve. The intermediate pressure turbine was double flow as was also the low pressure turbine. To achieve sufficient astern torque, the designers felt compelled to install a separate astern turbine and couple it to the high pressure pinion, followed by an astern drum in the low pressure turbine casing.

83

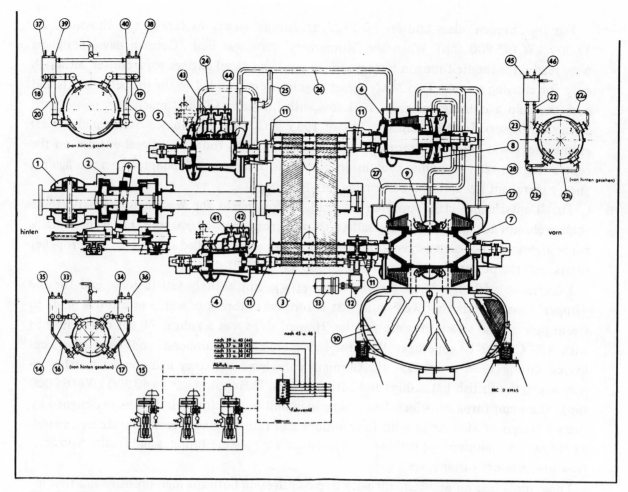

Fig. 65. Main turbines of the battlecruiser 'Scharnhorst'. Arrangement, G(HP+IP1+IP2+LP). Power 3× 40 300 kW (165 000 shp). Steam data, 60 bar, 450°C (855 lb/in², 860°F). Speed, 5 070 HP, 3 150 IP1/IP2, 2 400 LP, 280 prop. rev/min. All Curtis wheels had 4 nozzles and 4 separate nozzle valves. Propeller shafts could be uncoupled. Hydraulic manoeuvring of all control valves. Brown Boveri of Mannheim, 1958.

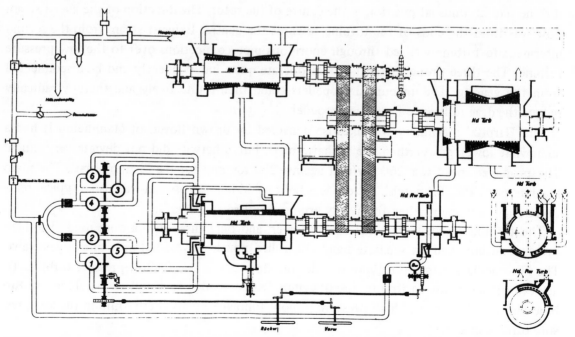

Fig. 66. Main turbines of the battleship 'Bismarck'. Arrangement G(HP+IP+LP). Power 3×33 800 kW 138 000 shp). Steam data 60 bar (855 lb/in²), 450°C (840°F). Speed, HP&IP 2 900 rev/min, LP 1 600 rev/min. Valves manoeuvred by cam shafts and handwheels. Six nozzle valves, one bypass valve. Double-flow intermediate pressure blading. Blohm & Voss, 1940.

When the German Navy began to expand its destroyer fleet at the end of the thirties, extremely high steam conditions were chosen right from the beginning, 73 bar up to 125 bar (1 045 to 1800 lb/in²), with 450°C (842°F) superheat. German land turbine manufacturers had a great deal of experience with high pressures and temperatures. But they were to learn the hard way that conditions at sea with astern operation and manoeuvring make quite different demands on marine turbines than those met with by land turbines. Experience with the German destroyer machinery was far from satisfactory.

Selection of the turbine arrangement jumped from one solution to another, see fig. 67. For the destroyers of 1936 vintage, three pinions were chosen as shown by "A". To obtain a good cruising performance, a geared cruising turbine that could be uncoupled was connected to the high pressure shaft. The low pressure pinion shaft was placed on top of the gear box, while the high and intermediate pressure pinions were placed at the sides of the gear. As all the turbines were placed forward of the gear box, there was insufficient space between the high and intermediate pressure turbines for the low pressure turbine. The designers therefore had to introduce an intermediate wheel between the high and intermediate pressure pinions and the main gear wheel. There was only one astern turbine in the low pressure turbine. It became apparent that the hydraulic coupling C had such a large torque that, even when running decoupled, the cruising turbine could easily overspeed.

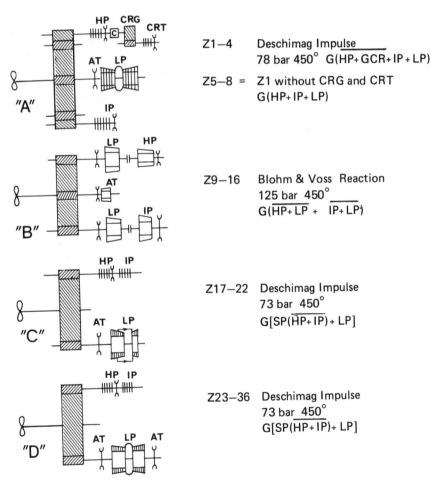

Fig. 67. Turbine arrangements of German destroyers during the Second World War.

The cruising turbine with its gear was therefore the left out in the destroyers of 1937 to 1938. The next destroyers had reaction turbines of Blohm & Voss design. The pressure was raised to 125 bar (1 800 lb/in²) with the installation of Benson boilers. As shown by fig. 67 "B", two parallel low pressure turbines were placed on either side of the gearbox and coupled in tandem to the high and intermediate pressure turbines respectively. The astern turbine had its own pinion on top of the gear. Experience with this arrangement proved to give an even worse availability than with the previous destroyers.

For the 1938 to 1939 series of destroyers, fig. 67 "C", 'Deschimag' had a second chance at the design. A series-parallel arrangement between the high and intermediate pressure blading on the same shaft was introduced. This arrangement had been patented by the Krupp-Germaniawerft in 1933, before which it had been used by the Japanese Navy. The low pressure turbine had an astern wheel, and an asymmetric double flow for ahead operation. The final destroyer types had a symmetrical low pressure turbine with an astern Curtis wheel at each end, as shown by fig. 67 "D".

In the same way as after the First World War, the German naval fleet was destroyed or annexed by the winning powers. The United States sent investigating commissions to Germany after the war to seek for any designs or developments worth taking up, and they made a short summary of their findings. Compared with American designs:

1. Fuel consumptions were higher.
2. Weight per unit power was considerably higher.
3. Space requirements were substantially greater per unit power.
4. Accessibility for inspection and overhaul was very much worse.
5. Availability established under battle conditions was very much worse than the American.
6. Only single reduction gears with intermediate bearings were used.
7. The gears used conservative tooth loadings, but had inferior material combinations. Thus manganese-silicon alloys were used instead of nickel alloys due to the shortage of nickel.

5.3   France and Italy — Inter-War and Second World War

French interest had never been so concentrated upon marine topics as had the British. In the Washington Treaty of 1921, France was permitted to increase her naval fleet up to 30 per cent of Great Britain's, but she never even came near this limit. At the beginning of the thirties, the French Navy consisted of 11 battleships — of which more than half were quite outmoded — no modern large cruisers, and only a few younger light cruisers, together with fifty or so smaller destroyers. Their propulsion machinery consisted largely of direct-driving or geared Parsons turbines.

When Mussolini began building up a large naval fleet of newer ships with superior speeds and performance, the French Admiralty was compelled to try to keep up with the Italians.

The Italian claims on Tunisia and Abyssinia speeded up their new-building. During the ten year period from 1923 to 1933, the Italians built 18 cruisers and 36 destroyers. The French answered with 14 cruisers and 46 destroyers. In 1933, the Italian yards began construction on four large battleships in the 'Cavour' and 'Littorio' classes. This prompted France to build four battleships in the 'Dunkerque' and 'Jean Bart' classes. At the end of the war in 1945, there were no modern ships left in the Italian Navy — they were all either sunk or captured. France on the other hand had a navy at the end of the war consisting of:

2 battleships of 26 500 tons of the 'Dunkerque' class

2 battleships of 35 000 tons of the 'Jean Bart' class

No aircraft carriers

10 cruisers of 10 000 tons

6 light cruisers, and

about 70 destroyers

The French ships had no specially remarkable qualities. They represented, however, European warship construction of top rank. Nevertheless, the great advances made in U.S. turbine technology had hardly been made use of. As with the Italian Navy, the importance of speed had been overrated — especially for destroyers, where the designers had tried to outdo each other in the use of high powers and speeds. For example, the destroyers of the 'Mogador' class reached speeds of over 42 knots during trials. Their nominal speed was 39 knots at a power of 2×34 000 kW (92 000 shp).

The French battleships from the latter part of the thirties had reaction turbines designed by Brown Boveri's subsidiary, Compagnie Electromécanique of Paris (CEM). They had four propeller shafts with a three-cylinder arrangement and single reduction gears. The cruisers had cross-compound turbines, usually with four shafts. Several cruisers had Parsons turbines, but some had impulse turbines of Rateau design. Among the destroyer machinery, more than half were of Parsons design, although Rateau impulse turbines were very well represented. A smaller number had Zoelly turbines made by the Schneider company. The large destroyers, as already mentioned, were in many respects prestige vessels, where high speeds were obtained at the cost of seaworthiness, armour and fighting power.

The state of French naval engineering for the period is demonstrated here by sectional drawings of the turbines and gears for the battleship 'Jean Bart' and the destroyers of the 'Mogador' class. The main data for these two ships are summarized below in Table 13.

Table 13.

Main data for 'Jean Bart' and 'Mogador'

Name Deliv. year	Tonnage	Power/1000		Speed knots	No. of shafts	Turbine arr.	Steam cond. bar/°C lb/in²/°F
		kW	shp				
Jean Bart 1949	35 000	121	165	32	4	G(HP+IP+LP) CEM	28/350°C 390/662°F
Mogador 1940	2880	68	92	39	2	G(HP+IP+2LP) Rateau	32/350°C 450/662°F

Figs 68, 69 and 70 show sectional drawings of the 'Jean Bart' turbines and fig. 71 shows the 'Jean Bart' gearing. The high pressure turbines, fig. 68, were not of the traditional Parsons drum type, but had drum forgings shrunk onto a shaft. In this way it was possible to use a relatively high speed of 3 000 rev/min. The intermediate pressure turbines, however, had the classic design and a slower speed of 2 700 rev/min. To cope with the large steam volumes in the final blading stages, the designers had chosen a lower speed of 1 600 rev/min for the low pressure turbines. The dimensions of the low pressure turbine were thus very large. Only the low pressure turbine had astern blading, one Curtis wheel and a reaction drum. The bull-wheel was made of steel castings with forged wheel rims bolted to the flat web

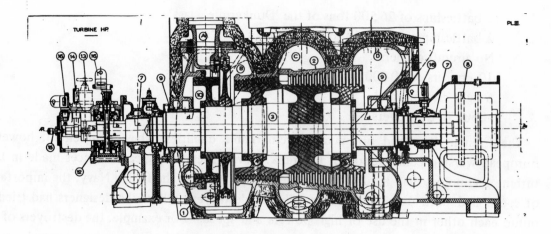

Fig. 68. High pressure turbine of the battleship, 'Jean Bart'. Steam data, 28 bar, 350°C (390 lb/in^2, 662°F). Speed 3 000 rev/min. Designed by CEM, 1940 to 1941.

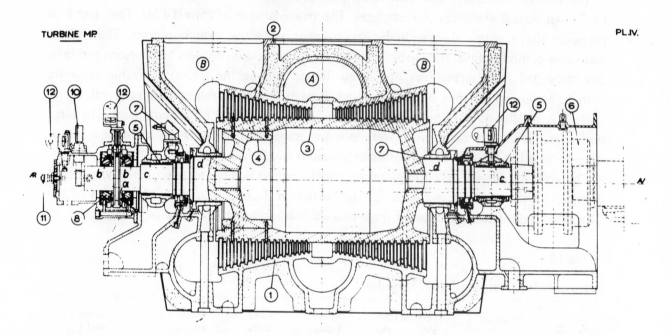

Fig. 69. Intermediate pressure turbine of the battleship, 'Jean Bart'. Speed 2 500 rev/min.

plates and the conical inner webs. All the pinions had intermediate bearings, as the reduction ratio was as high as 1:13. Compared with U.S. practice, the pinion loadings were relatively low, approx. K=5 bar (72 lb/in^2).

The Rateau turbine designs for the 'Mogador' class of destroyers were excellent examples of the foremost European pre-war engineering. The two ships in the class were launched in 1936 and 1937, entered service just before the German break-through and were sunk by their own navy in 1943, Their official powers were 2×33 800 kW (92 000 shp) but during trials the machinery was pushed up to 2×43 500 kW (118 300 shp) for a short period. By this means, a record of 43 1/2 knots was achieved, which has probably never been bettered by any warship of the displacement type. The machinery arrangement was unusual, and consisted of four main single-reduction turbines, and two geared declutchable cruising turbines. By splitting the propeller torque over four pinions, a gear of modest dimensions was ob-

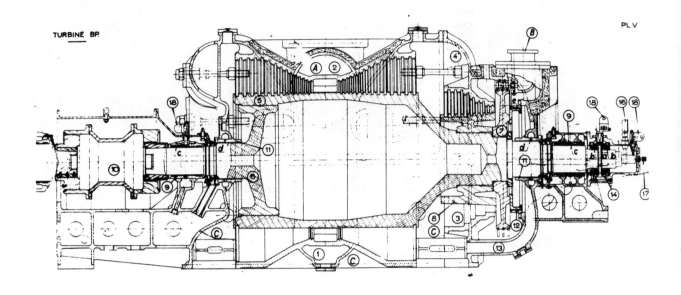

Fig. 70. Low pressure and astern turbines of the battleship, 'Jean Bart'. Speed 1 600 rev/min.

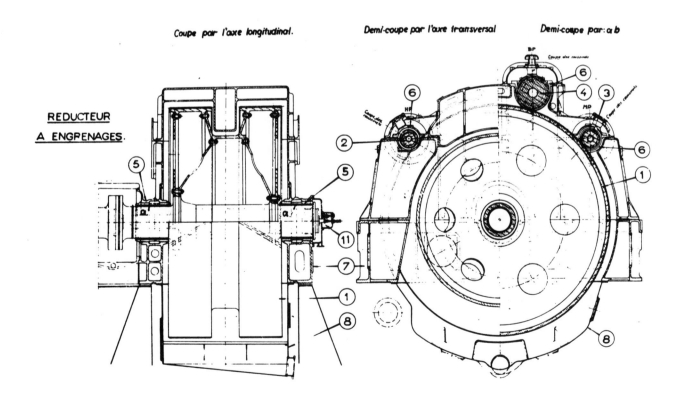

Fig. 71. Reduction gearing of the battleship 'Jean Bart'. 2=high pressure pinion,
3=intermediate pressure pinion, 4=low pressure pinion.

Turbine HP
Coupe Longitudinale d'Ensemble

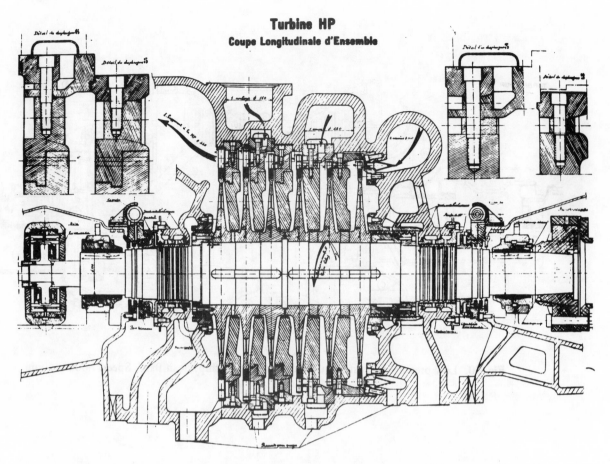

Fig. 72. High pressure turbine for 'Mogador'. 3 830 rev/min, 32 bar, 350°C (450 lb/in^2, 660°F).

Turbine MP
Coupe longitudinale d'Ensemble

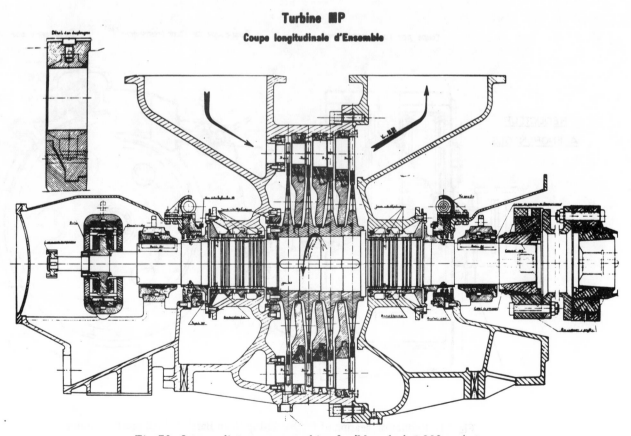

Fig. 73. Intermediate pressure turbine for 'Mogador'. 3 830 rev/min.

tained having a main wheel diameter of only 2.7 metres, despite the high output. The pinions had intermediate bearings, and the tooth loadings were moderate, not exceeding K=5.3 bar (77 lb/in^2) at normal power.

The main machinery was arranged G(HP+IP+2LP). The high and intermediate pressure turbines were placed at the after end and to the sides of the gear casing, while the two low pressure turbines were placed forward of the gear with the pinions so situated that a large common condenser had room under the low pressure casings. Steam conditions were 32 bar, 350°C (450 lb/in^2, 662°F). The gearing was largely similar to that described for the 'Jean Bart', fig. 71.

The high and intermediate pressure turbines were impulse type with six and four shrunk-on discs respectively, as shown in figs 72 and 73. The moving blades were of Rateau type with axial rectangular blade fastenings seated in milled groves. They were fastened by axial pins peened half-and-half in the blade fastening and discs, respectively. The high pressure turbine had two by-pass valves which admitted steam to before stages 3 and 5 respectively.

Although the low pressure turbines were in parallel, they were not the same, figs 74 and 75. Steam entered the low pressure turbine, LP1, from the intermediate turbine and expanded first through two single impulse stages. After these, the steam divided so that 1/3 passed the subsequent LP1 blading to the condenser. The remaining 2/3 was led from LP1 to LP2 via a cross-over pipe, and expanded through the double-flow ahead blading in LP2, fig. 75.

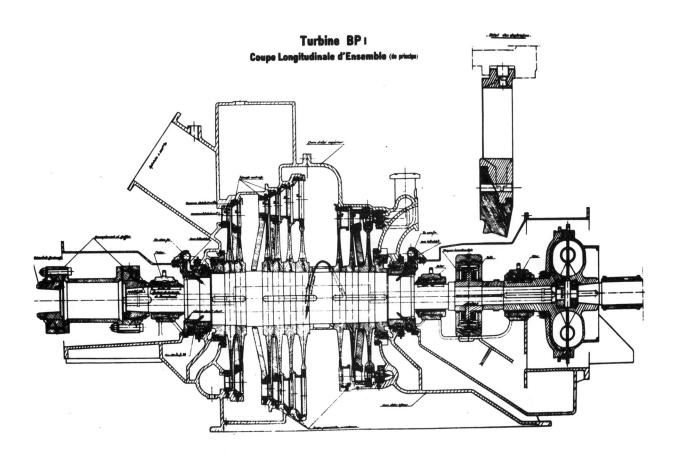

Turbine BP I
Coupe Longitudinale d'Ensemble (de principe)

Fig. 74. Low pressure turbine No. 1 for 'Mogador'. 3 230 rev/min. Entire steam flow passed the first two impulse wheels, but only 1/3 to the subsequent four single wheels.

91

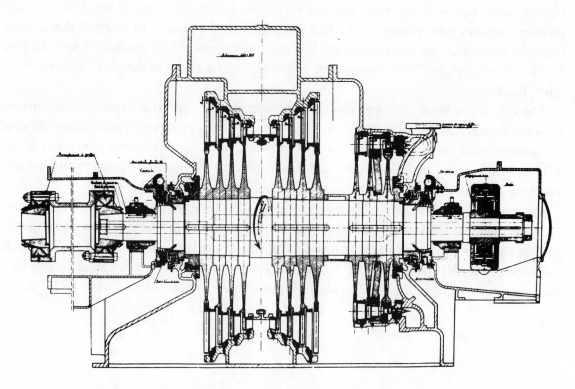

Turbine BP2
Coupe Longitudinale d'Ensemble

Fig. 75. Low pressure turbine No. 2 for 'Mogador'. The double-flow turbine received steam from the first two impulse stages of LP turbine No. 1, and was coupled via a Vulkan coupling and gearing to the cruising turbine.

LP1 and LP2 had astern turbines in parallel, each consisting of a Curtis wheel and two single stages. At normal ahead power, the speed was 3 830 rev/min for the high and intermediate pressure turbines and 3 230 rev/min for the low pressure turbines. Propeller speed was then 370 rev/min.

The cruising units consisted of two turbines connected in series, figs 76 and 77, having four and five single impulse stages respectively. Speeds were high, 8 690 and 7 510 rev/min, respectively, at maximum cruising power. The turbine discs were machined out of the solid rotor forgings and were thus able to resist the stresses at the high operating speeds.

At 23 knots and below, the steam passed through the two cruising turbines to the normal steam inlet of the high pressure turbine. At 26 knots and 15 600 kW (21 200 shp), the highest permissible speeds for the cruising turbines were reached and the units were automatically uncoupled. The cruising turbines were connected via gearing to the low pressure turbine rotors through Vulkan hydraulic couplings. At speeds over 26 knots, there was risk of the cruising turbines overspeeding, so their steam supply was automatically cut off and the hydraulic couplings were emptied at the same time.

The 'Mogador' destroyer machinery was regarded at the time as having the best weight and performance data in the European navies. They had, despite single reduction gearing for the main machinery and relatively conservative steam data, a performance not far from those of the corresponding American units. The cruising turbine arrangement, however, was a little risky if the automatic coupling did not work.

Turbine de Croisière I.
Coupe Longitudinale d'Ensemble

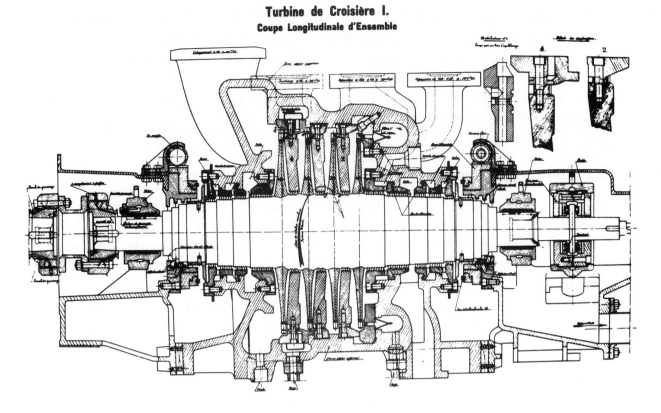

Fig. 76. First cruising turbine for 'Mogador'. Speed 8 960 rev/min. Coupled to LP turbine No. 1 through gearing.

Turbine de Croisière II. — Coupe Longitudinale d'Ensemble

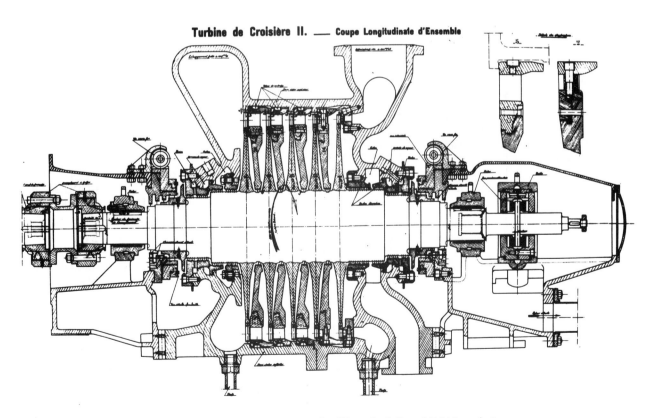

Fig. 77. Second cruising turbine for 'Mogador'. Speed 7 510 rev/min. Coupled to LP turbine No. 2 through gearing.

Due to the French capitulation, the contributions of the French Navy during the Second World War were few and not very glamorous. The British attack on 'Jean Bart' and 'Richelieu' was a great tragedy for the French naval personnel. Even if the level of French marine turbine manufacture did not match the American, it was well on a par with the best of European. The French, on the other hand, were leaders in respect of pressurized boiler furnaces, in which they were pioneers for naval applications.

5.4 Post-War naval shipbuilding in continental Europe

Only a few warships were built to begin with in the countries of western continental Europe after the end of the war. Since the beginning of the 'Cold War' at the end of the forties, NATO's defence forces have been built up and have brought about a considerable new-construction of naval fighting vessels. Through NATO, American weaponry and machinery technology could be transferred to Europe. Robot missiles, remote-controlled torpedoes and advanced submarine techniques became available, as well as NATO's own well-developed designs. As with the British Navy, the trend has been away from battleships and cruisers to

Table 14.

Turbine-driven naval ships in the NATO fleets delivered 1955 – 1980

Deliv. year	No. – Class	Country Ship type	Tonnage	Power/1000 kW	Power/1000 shp	Turbine design	Machinery type
1956–60	10 – E52	F – Fr	1 250	15	20	Rateau	2 CC–SR
1957–62	13 – T47,53,56	F – D	2 750	46	63	–"–	2 CC–SR
1959	1 – Colbert	F – C	8 500	63,5	86	CEM	2 CC–SR
1961–63	2 – Clemenceau	F – AC	27 300	93	126	CEM	2 CC–SR
1963	1 – La Resolute	F – C	10 000	63,5	86	Rateau	2 CC–DR
1967	2 – Suffren	F – D	3 800	40	54	–"–	2 CC–DR
1973	1 – C65	F – D	3 500	14,7	20	–"–	2 CC–DR
1978	3 – C70	F – D	3 800	38	52	Rolls Royce	CODOG + CP
1958	2 – Impetuoso	I – D	2 755	48	65	CDT	2 CC–SR
1963–73	4 – Audace	I – D	3200/3600	53/54	70/73	CDT	2 CC–DR
1964	2 – Andrea Doria	I – D	5 000	44	60	CDT	2 CC–DR
1964–69	1 – Vittori Veneto	I – HeC	7 500	54	73	Tosi	2 CC–DR
1965	1 – San Georgi	I – D	3 950	23	31	Tosi	CODOG–CP
1968	4 – Albina	I – Fr	2 700	23	31	Tosi	CODOG–CP
1977	4 – Lupo	I – Fr	2 500	43	58	Fiat LM2500	CODOG–CP
1955–58	1 – Holland	NL – D	2 500	33	45	Werkspoor	2 CC–SR
1956–58	8 – Friesland	NL – D	2 200	44	60	–"–	2 CC–SR
1967	6 – Speil	NL – D	2 700	22	30	–"–	2 CC–DR
1975–76	2 – Tromp	NL – D	4 300	43	58	Rolls Royce	COGOG–CP
1978–80	8 – Kortenaer	NL – Fr	3 500	43	58	–"–	COGOG–CP
1961–64	6 – Köln	G – Fr	2 100	19	26	BBC–MAN	CODAG–CP
1964–68	4 – Hamburg	G – D	3 400	50	68	Wahodag	2 CC–DR
1969–70	3 – Adams	G – D	3 370	51,5	70	GE	2 CC–DR

F = France   I = Italy   NL = The Netherlands   G = West Germany

D = Destroyer   AC = Aircraft carrier   HeC = Helicopter Cruiser   Fr = Frigate
C = Cruiser   CC = Cross-compound turbines   SR = Single reduct.   DR = Double reduct.
CODOG = Combined diesel or gas turbine   CODAG = Combined diesel and gas turbine
CP = Controllable-pitch propeller   GE = General Electric USA   CDT = Cantieri del Tireno
CEM = Companie Electroméchanique

lighter vessels. Only a few aircraft carriers have been built, but on the other hand a considerable number of destroyers, frigates and corvettes have been produced in France, Italy, Holland and West Germany. Not until the sixties did the U.S. technology with high speed rotors and double reduction gears break through. In the middle of the sixties, the first gas turbines were installed in destroyers and frigates. The last steam-propelled ship was delivered during the seventies.

Table 14 gives a resumé of the ships built for NATO in France, Italy, Holland and West Germany.

5.5 Brown Boveri machinery for Inter-War Soviet battlecruisers

Greatest ever power on one shaft

It was decreed that during Stalin's third five-year plan, Soviet Russia would build up a powerful naval fleet. Accordingly, in 1935, funds were appropriated for the construction of four giant battleships of approximately 60 000 tons, as well as two large, fast battlecruisers of 35 000 tons. Russian shipyards had indeed built battleships before the Revolution, but there was no experience of modern naval technology in the Soviet. For the battleships, the Admiralty in Leningrad contacted Gibbs & Cox in New York. The U.S. government even granted these consultants permission to carry out the preliminary project work on the battleships. With the U.S. battleships as example, turbo-electric machinery was proposed. Three of these vessels had their keels laid prior to the start of the Second World War, and work on their machinery had commenced at the Leningrad engine works.

For the battlecruisers, the Russian Admiralty had asked for and received the basic design and specifications from the well-known Italian shipyard, Ansaldo of Trieste. The ships were to be larger than any battleship or cruiser then building. In addition, they were to be capable of extremely high speeds. The battleships were to have a power considerably higher than that of the 'Hood'. They were to have a total power of 170 000 kW (231 000 shp) on three shafts. The battlecruisers were to have two shafts and a total power of 113 000 kW (154 000 shp). These figures may be compared with the U.S. battleships of the 'North Dakota' class, which were being planned at about the same time. These were to be of 38 000 tons with a total power of 97 000 kW (130 000 shp) on four shafts.

As can be seen from Table 15, the Russian project was most extreme. Even to this very day, ships have yet to be built with powers exceeding these Russian installations of 56 700 kW (70 000 shp) per shaft. Only the Japanese 'Yamato' class, designed before the Second World War, was of a size comparable to the projected Russian battleships; but the power of the Soviet ships was 54 per cent higher! The British Navy never had plans for battleships larger than those permitted by the London Treaty, i.e. 45 000 tons. Not until the giant U.S. aircraft carriers came were ships as large, or larger, built with higher total power and with about the same power per standard ton. If Gibbs & Cox really prescribed a power of 3x56 700 kW for the Russian battleships is questionable. The very radical designers at Ansaldo, however, *may* have specified those enormous powers for the battlecruisers.

For some reason it was decided that the two battlecruisers should have turbo-mechanical machinery in contrast to the battleships. The Russian Navy had no gear-cutting machines at their disposal sufficiently large to manufacture the reduction gears. For the two battlecruisers, therefore, the Russian Admiralty decided to procure tenders from several of the best known producers of marine turbines. The specified propeller speed at full power was

Table 15.

High-powered engines for battleships, battlecruisers and later American aircraft carriers.

Ship St. tons	Year Country	Power/1000 kW	shp	No. of shafts knots	Power per shaft shp	Turbine arr. Steam cond.	Shp/ St./ton	Thrust* per prop. shaft, tons
Hood 41 200	BC 1918 GB	107	144	4 31	36 000	G(HP+LP)/G($\overline{HP+CR}$+LP) 17 bar/sat	3,5	117
Saratoga 37 700	AC 1925 USA	134	180	4 33	45 000	4 TG-8 EM 22 bar/260°	4,8	137
North Carolina 37 500	BS 1940 USA	90	121	4 28	30 250	GG(HP+LP) 42 bar/455°	3,2	109
Yamato 62 300	BS 1940 J	112	150	4 27	37 500	G(HP+GCR+2LP) 25 bar/350°	2,4	141
Scharnhorst 34 800	BC 1936 G	121	165	3 32	55 000	G(HP+IP1+IP2+LP) 50 bar/450°	4,7	169
Iowa 48 100	BS 1942 USA	158	212	4 32.5	53 000	GG(HP+LP) 42 bar/455°	4,4	167
Sovyetsky Ukraina 60 000	BS (1941) USSR	170	231	3 30	77 000	3 TG-6 EM 35 bar/370°	3,9	256
Kronstadt 35 240	BC (1941) USSR	113	154	2 33	77 000	G[SP(HP+IP)+2LP] 35 bar/370°	4,4	233
Kitty Hawk 61 000	AC 1960 USA	209	280	4 33	70 000	GG[SP(HP+IP)+LP] 84 bar/510°	4,6	213
Nimitz 83 000	AC 1972 USA	209	280	4 33	70 000	GG(HP+LP) 30 bar/sat	3,4	213

BC = Battlecruiser   AC = Aircraft carrier   BS = Battleship

*Propeller efficiency assumed at 70 %. No thrust reduction factor.

252 rev/min, and the steam pressure was 35 bar (495 lb/in^2) with 370°C (700°F) superheat temperature. Table 15 shows the large step involved in going from the then highest power of 33 600 kW (45 000 shp) per shaft in the 'Saratoga' to the 70 per cent higher power required by the Russians. Several manufacturers, however, regarded themselves competent to design a geared turbine with four rotors for the specified power.

What surprises a naval architect, however, is the courage of the Russian propeller experts of those days, who dared to undertake to produce propellers capable of withstanding the enormous propeller thrusts proposed. Brown Boveri's engineers were very sceptical that any European manufacturer would dare to take on and give guarantees for propellers to resist thrusts of the order of 230 to 260 tons. At the time the machinery was ordered, no ship had operated with propeller thrusts greater than one half of the Russian values. Not even the U.S. aircraft carriers of the seventies and eighties were to have higher propeller loadings. It must also be realized that 30 years of research in cavitation and propeller design lie between the Russian project and the giant American aircraft carriers.

A prolonged fight for the Russian order was begun. Brown Boveri of Baden was not to be scared off by the task ahead. In the thirties, the marine department at Baden held a leading position in the European development of naval turbines. They had already planned unit powers of about 40 000 kW (54 000 shp) for the German battleships, and around 30 000 kW (41 000 shp) for the French.

During the author's employment with Brown Boveri, Baden, he got the chance of assisting at the inception of a number of very interesting orders for marine turbines. In 1936, an order was placed by the Japanese Navy for machinery for the auxiliary vessel which is described in Chapter 4.

In 1935, a challenging enquiry had arrived from the Soviet central purchasing agency in Moscow, 'Maschinoimport'. It was for the projected battlecruisers 'Kronstadt' and 'Sevastopol' already mentioned.* After long drawn-out negotiations, an order was placed with Brown Boveri for this machinery.

The author took part in the battle of tenders between some of the world's larger marine turbine manufacturers. The Depression had hit the USA and Europe hard. All turbine manufacturers had more or less empty workshops. The Russian buyers knew how to use the situation to their own advantage. During the final round of negotiations, very strict guarantees were demanded together with comprehensive workshop trials, testing the units up to an output of at least 11 000 kW.

The arrangement first proposed by Brown Boveri, fig. 78, was similar to that planned for the large German battleships (later to be the 'Scharnhorst' and 'Gneisenau'). With the gear-cutting facilities then available at Baden, it was clear that four pinions had to be used to obtain the power output at acceptable turbine speeds. The new hobber did not allow greater wheel diameters than 4 metres (157 in). In was therefore convenient to split up the heat drop between four turbine rotors, each coupled to its own pinion. The low pressure turbine thus became very large and ran at a low speed to pass the tremendous steam flows through only two reaction drums. The cross-over pipes from the second intermediate turbine to the low pressure turbine grew to such dimensions that space problems became serious as the low pressure turbine already took up most of the available room.

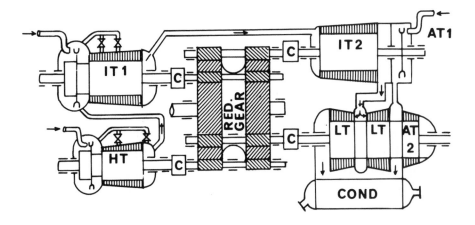

Fig. 78. Proposed arrangement in the 1935—36 tender to Machinoimport for 56 620 kW (77 000 shp).

* Presumably the intended names, although others occur in correspondence and literature.

At higher powers, the proposal required bypass valves to be opened in the high pressure and first intermediate pressure turbines. In addition, at about half speed, live steam was to be admitted to the Curtis wheel in the first intermediate pressure turbine. During the opening discussions in Moscow, it became clear that Brown Boveri was still in the running, but that the weight was greater than that of certain competitors, and the full speed steam consumption had to be improved. Walter Boveri, the managing director, has described in his memoirs the difficult situation at Baden during those years. The amount of work in the factories was quite insufficient. The management did everything they could to win this important order for the Baden plant.

A number of radical changes were made to the project drawings in 1937. The high and intermediate pressure turbines were altered to a series-parallel arrangement. Two low pressure turbines, each with an astern turbine, were placed forward of the gear box. A much more favourable arrangement was thereby obtained. The speed of the low pressure turbines could be increased, giving smaller blade heights at the four exhausts. Both cruising and full speed consumptions were improved and a considerable weight reduction could be made. After several rounds of arduous negotiations, each with more price reductions, the order was placed. It may also not reflect too well on B.B.C.'s present standing with, say, the U.S.A., even though at the time Switzerland as a neutral country had no reason to imagine that giving the Soviets marine technical "Knowhow" could later be viewed critically by the West.

Fig. 79 shows the arrangement. All rotors were typical light-weight Brown Boveri design. The drums were shrunk-on and bolted to the flange of the shaft end. The Curtis wheel was forged solid with the shaft. The astern turbines in the low pressure turbines consisted of a Curtis wheel followed by a single stage. The high pressure turbine ran at 3 125 rev/min at full speed, and the other rotors ran at 2 920 rev/min.

The couplings were of fine-tooth type. The gear, fig. 80, was impressively large, but was, for the power transmitted, very light. The wheel rims on the bull wheel were bolted to the web plates, which in turn were bolted to flanges on the light, hollow main shaft. The condensers had single-pass cooling water and were placed for-and-aft under the low pressure turbines. Both the low pressure turbines and gear casing were to a large extent of welded plate construction. Because of the high reduction ratio, all pinions had intermediate bearings. The high pressure pinion had a gear ratio of 12.4, and the remainder a ratio of 11.6. Tooth loadings were moderate and around $K=6$ bar (85 lb/in^2). Brown Boveri tried to have all turbine rotors of welded construction in accordance with Dr Meyer's patent, but the customer refused to accept this.

Fig. 81 shows the schematic arrangement of manoeuvring valves. The high pressure turbine had three nozzle valves, 1, 2 and 3, and two parallel bypass valves, 6. The intermediate pressure turbine similarly had three nozzle valves, 4, 5 and 7, but no bypass valves. The series-parallel changeover was done by the butterfly valves 8a and 8b, which led exhaust steam from the high pressure turbine to the intermediate or low pressure turbines respectively. The astern turbines each had three nozzle valves, 11, 12 and 13.

All valves were controlled by cam shafts actuated by hydraulic rotary pistons. The emergency system of the unit operated two stop valves, one for ahead and one for astern. The emergency system used non-inflammable hydraulic oil. The unit was manoeuvred either from the turbine room or from a common central control room by hydraulic remote control.

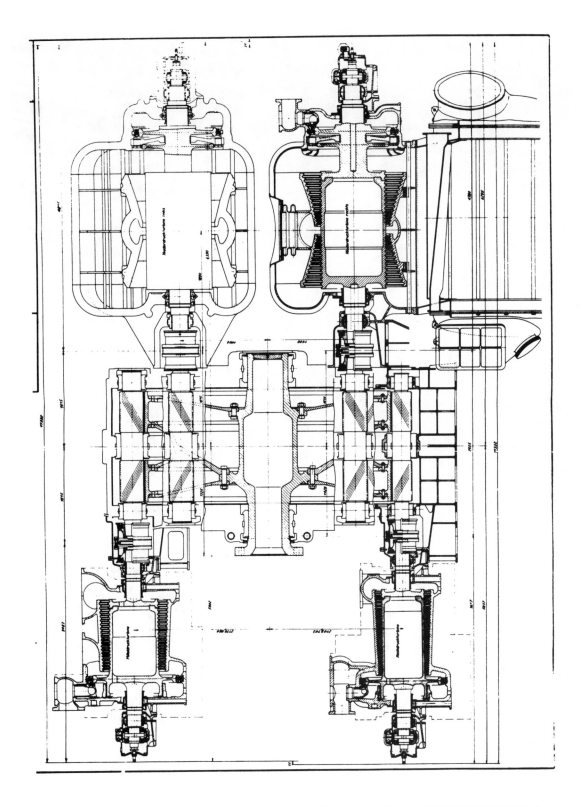

Fig. 79. Section through the main machinery of the 'Kronstadt'. Power 56 620 kW (77 000 shp). Propeller speed 252 rev/min. Steam data 35 bar, 370°C (495 lb/in^2, 700°F). Series-parallel arrangement of HP and IP turbines. Delivered 1940.

Fig. 80. Bull wheel of the 'Kronstadt'. Diameter 4 metres (157 in). Speed 252 rev/min.

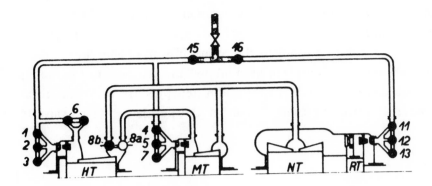

Fig. 81. Control system for the 'Kronstadt'.
1, 2 and 3 are nozzle valves on the HP turbine. 4, 5, and 7 are nozzle valves on the IP turbine. 6 is two bypass valves on the HP turbine. 8a is a butterfly valve in the exhaust from HP to IP turbine. 8b is a butterfly valve to the LP turbines. 11, 12 and 13 are nozzle valves to the two astern turbines (6 total). 15 is the emergency valve for ahead operation. 16 is emergency valve for astern operation.

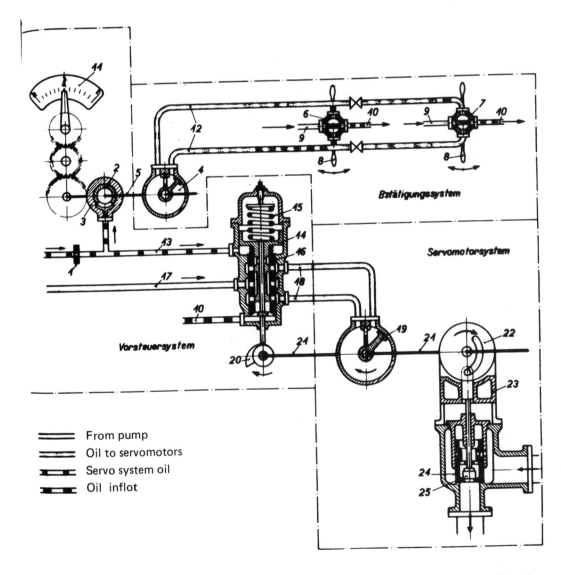

Fig. 82. Remote-controlled manoeuvring gear for nozzle and bypass valves, as well as butterfly valves for series-parallel operation, on the 'Kronstadt'.

The system, as shown in fig. 82 and 83, was rather complicated. Nozzle and bypass valves on the ahead and astern turbines were opened successively by a control system consisting of control valves 6, 7, 8, which positioned the rotary piston 4. This turned the presetting oil slots in the control unit 2, 3, so the required oil pressure was obtained in the pipe 13. As the pressure rose, the distributor slide 14, 16, admitted pressure oil to the rotary piston 19, which progressively turned the cam 22 and set the nozzle or bypass valve to give the required steam flow.

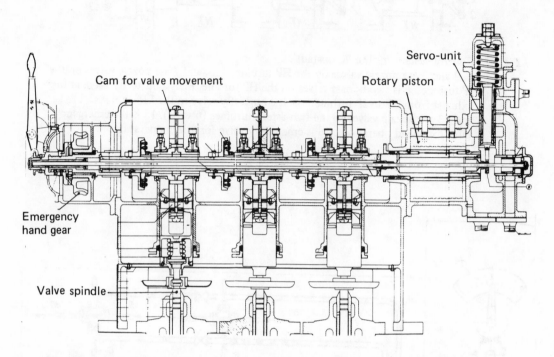

Fig. 83. Rotary piston and camshaft control for three nozzle valves on the 'Kronstadt'.

The first unit, fig. 84, was tested during 1939 to 1940. The customer required the unit to be tested under the highest power possible. A large water brake was therefore procured for this purpose from A.E.G., Berlin. About 11 000 kW (15 000 shp) could thus be absorbed on the test bed. Comprehensive tests and manoeuvring at all speeds up to the maximum were carried out. All manoeuvers were done with the central hydraulic control gear. The final tests were made under the supervision of the nestor of steam turbine technology, Professor Aurel Stodola. The tests were entirely satisfactory after a number of adjustments were made to the hydraulic control gear. Among other things, the non–inflammable hydraulic fluid caused a deal of trouble. The first two units for the cruiser 'Kronstadt' could be shipped to the Leningrad shipyard in time to get across the border just before Hitler opened his invasion of Russia. One of the units for the cruiser 'Sevastopol' was delivered to the Nikolayev shipyard in the Crimea. The last unit lay a long while in storage in Switzerland before it was scrapped. Both battlecruisers were destroyed during the war by the Germans and also by the Russian troops during the evacuation of the Crimea. The ships came no farther than the slipways, and the machinery was probably never installed. These were the final chapters in four years technical development of the highest quality in Switzerland. A better example of splendid engineering science brought to disintegration by human folly and misery would be hard to find.

Fig. 84. One of the 'Kronstadt' units assembled on the test bed and connected to a large water brake. Unit is complete with condensers, remote-control gear and instrument panel.

5.6 Incidents from the author's assignment at Brown Boveri 1936 to 1940

In the spring of 1937 an unbelievably hectic time began in the marine department at Baden. Delivery time for the Russian battlecruiser machinery was only just over two years. To get the design drawings out in time, the work was split up over several departments. At times, about a hundred draughtsmen and designers were occupied with the Soviet order.

When the designs for the low pressure turbines were to be approved by Maschinoimport's experts, the design department got a rude shock, but at the same time a very useful lesson. According to the contract guarantees, the critical speeds of all rotors were to be at least thirty per cent higher than the maximum operating speed. After checking the drawings and caculations, the customer stated that Brown Boveri had calculated wrongly and that the margin above maximum speed was at the most 15 per cent.

The Russian experts were exceedingly clever theoreticians and had a method of calculation that was far in advance of the classic Stodola-Grammel graphical method. In the latter, no account was taken of deformations in the end discs between the shafts and drum cylinders. The Russian experts had managed to calculate the membrane deformation in these discs and thereby arrived at a lower critical speed than the traditional calculations predicted. Brown Boveri's leading mathematician, Axel Mehldahl (later professor), found that the Russian calculations were correct. He developed his own calculation method, which appeared to agree with the Russian. The author, who is more practical than theoretical, made a model and carried out rotating tests on it. The results were even more pessimistic than those from the Russian and professor Mehldahl's calculations.

The company, however, was lucky. The shaft forgings had not yet been completed at the steel works, and could be thickened up so that the guaranteed critical speed could be achieved. The thicker end discs gave smaller membrane deformations. The customer agreed to this procedure, but required that the critical speed be verified by vibration and spin tests. When the vibration test was carried out in the works one evening, without the inspectors being present, it was found that despite the reinforcements to the rotor, it chose to vibrate with a strong resonance just near the maximal operating speed. A spin test with the rotor in its own bearings confirmed this result.

A week of anxious perplexity and endless internal discussions followed. A number of low pressure rotors of similar design that had been in operation were checked out and it was found that the true critical speed was 30 to 50 per cent lower than that calculated by the commonly accepted Stodola-Grammel method. Thus Brown Boveri, and later General Electric, found that the bearing supports for the rotor were anything but fixed in space, as assumed in the calculation model. The supports were resilient with elastic deflections of the same order as the shaft deflections. But the wrongly calculated low pressure rotors that were now so carefully checked had worked without difficulty for many years. A complaint had been made only in one case, but then it had been a question of poor balancing. When the balancing had been corrected, even that rotor had behaved properly.

It was agreed, however, that it would be quite impossible to explain this situation to the customer and still have him approve the design. The only possibility seemed to be to redesign and manufacture new rotors. To find out how low pressure rotors behaved on various elastic bearing supports, a number of tests were carried out at night. Soft supports naturally lowered the critical speeds. With a suitable elasticity, it might be possible to demonstrate vibration and spin tests over the entire speed range where a critical speed could not be detected. Suitable elastic and damping supports were built. Spin tests were then made with the inspectors present, who gave them their full approval. These experiences with low pressure rotors showed that the classical methods of calculation were quite unreliable for large rotors, where the elasticity of the bearing supports had a large influence.

The tests showed that if the rotor had sufficient damping, e.g. in bearing oil films, and if it was correctly and adequately balanced, there was little risk involved in having a critical speed within the running range. When the General Electric had the same experience during the fifties and resolved the consequences stemming from it, it soon became their rule to make over-critical shafts also for marine turbines. The aim was then to place the fundamental critical speed at about 60 per cent of the maximum operating speed.

By 1938, the renowned steel works of Witkowitz had begun to cast the thin conical side webs to the big gear wheels. These were four metres in diameter, had large reinforced cut-out reliefs and were to be as thin as possible to save weight. The specifications required all steel castings to be free from defects with no slag inclusions, surface faults or cavities. To cast such an enormous conical plate was such a difficult task that only the Witkowitz works dared to accept the order. The first large plate was scrapped by the Russian inspectors because of a few fairly shallow slag inclusions. These could quite easily have been chiselled out, according to the foundry engineer.

The next plate was a masterpiece of casting without the slightest defect. The steel works never managed to repeat this masterly performance during the ensuing casts. The inspectors scrapped disc after disc. All of them, on the assurance of Witkowitz, with only insignificant blemishes. Finally, Witkowitz's patience ran out. They telegraphed to Baden that either the order be abandoned, or the customer must accept the Lloyd's representative as the inspection authority. How Dr Meyer managed to get the stiff, meticulous inspector sent home is not known. The steel discs were, however, despatched and found to be well-nigh perfect.

6. WARSHIP MACHINERY FROM THE SWEDISH DE LAVAL COMPANY

6.1 The Twenties – A slack decade for de Laval naval turbines

It was apparent in 1924 that the epoch of turbine-driven merchant shipping was finished for the foreseeable future in Scandinavia. Admittedly, steam ships with reciprocating machinery were still being built in considerable numbers, but diesel engines were fast gaining the upper hand and turbine propulsion was conspicuous by its absence from shipyard order books. Reciprocating steam engines still had a number of advantages over diesel engines. Coal was cheap in comparison with oil, and on certain routes the steam engine was superior in operation. Such was the case for ships navigating in ice, as on the Sweden – Finland run and trade routes to Northern Sweden, where their manoeuvrability gave them ascendancy. Scandinavian yards launched 63 steamships and 17 motorships in 1924.

In 1928 the figures were 24 steamships and 27 motorships. Those steamships that were fitted with modernised triple or double compound engines often had exhaust steam turbines. Several systems were developed during the twenties and thirties for such combined engines. The German Bauer-Wach system connected the exhaust steam turbine by hydraulic couplings and gearing to the propeller shaft. Brown Boveri in Switzerland, and other European builders, connected the exhaust steam turbine to the propeller shaft by gearing and flexible couplings. The Lindholmen yard coupled the turbine to an electric generator. The electric power that could not be used by the ship's own circuits was used in an electric superheater between the high and low pressure cylinders. Götaverken developed a compact design where the exhaust steam turbine drove a steam compressor, which raised the pressure and superheated the steam between the high and low pressure cylinders. De Laval built a number of such steam compressor units for the Götaverken system, but none of the exhaust steam turbine systems became a real success on the market.

With the successful impulse turbine designs for the 'Wrangel' and 'Wachtmeister', delivered in 1918, the Swedish de Laval Company (de Lavals Ångturbin) had gained international distinction – which however was of short duration. Compared to the reaction turbines of Parsons in Britain, Westinghouse and Bethlehem in the U.S., Brown Boveri and Blohm & Voss in Germany, the de Laval turbines were equal in steam economy and superior in weight and operational flexibility. The impulse turbine of Brown–Curtis in Britain, AEG-Vulcan, Zoelly-MAN in Germany, and Rateau in France were on average somewhat heavier and had not quite the same quality of gearing. General Electric of U.S. had somewhat heavier designs than the Swedish company, but at least comparable performance and quality. Before World War 2, the American de Laval Company had approval from Bureau of Ships to deliver only naval turbine gearing. The de Laval turbine designs with bulb-and-shank blade fastenings were not accepted in the U.S. Navy.

In the twenties and thirties hardly any exports of naval turbines existed, with a few exceptions for deliveries from Parsons. Nations with their own designs or manufacturing facilities with licences from abroad favoured the home market.

For the Swedish de Laval with only a very small home market, it was more or less impossible to build up a sufficient export production, in spite of competitive design and good manufacturing quality. As the Swedish Navy did not order naval ships for quite a period after the First World War, de Laval had to place naval and mercantile marine turbine production in hibernation for several years.

6.2 De Laval turbines for the Swedish Navy

It took nine years after the small destroyers, 'Wrangel' and 'Wachmeister', with de Laval turbines were commissioned in 1918 before the Swedish Navy ordered any new destroyers.

The sister ships, 'Ehrensköld' and 'Nordenskjöld' of 1927/28, were of more international stature and twice as large, displacing about 1 000 tons. The 'Ehrensköld' turbines had a power of 2×9 500 kW (26 000 shp) and became prototypes for the machineries of subsequent turbine ships in the Swedish Navy for many years.

The development of the de Laval turbines for the Swedish Navy is summarized in Table 16. De Laval's design principles from 'Wrangel' onwards were retained with only small changes. The units are enlarged, adapted and improved in steps, but many of the design details remained unchanged into the fifties.

Table 16.

De Laval machinery for the Swedish Navy

Ship	Year of trial	No. of Ships	Output kW shp	Steam cond. bar/°C lb/in²/°F	Speed rev/min HP	LP	Prop.	Turbine arr. No. of impulse wheels C=Curtis S=single HP Cruise/Full speed		LP	Steam cons. full speed kg/kWh lb/shph	Spec. wt kg/kW lb/shp Total deliv.
1 Wrangel D	1918	2	2×4800 13000	19 260 sat	3600	3600	450	1C+1S	4S	4S	8.3/6.9 13.6/11.3	7.5 12.3
2 Ehrensköld D	1927	2	2×9500 26000	19 260 sat	3140	2730	450	2C	4S	4S	7.9/6.8 13.0/11.2	6.1 10.0
3 Klas Horn D	1932	2	2×9500 26000	19 260 sat	3140	2730	450	2C	4S	4S	7.9/6.8 13.0/11.2	5.7 9.4
4 Gotland CR	1934	1	2×12000 33000	21 260 sat	2600	2225	310	2C	4S	4S	7.5/6.7 12.3/11.0	5.7 9.4
5 Jägaren PB	1935	4	1×2650 3600	19 260 sat	3610		450	2C+6S		–	–	–
6 Göteborg D	1936	6	2×11800 32000	26/350 360/662	3500	3000	490	2C	4S	4S	6.7/5.7 11.0/9.4	5.0 8.2
7 Arholma M	1939	14	2×1200 3200	19 260 sat	4200		365	1C+7S			7.5/6.5 12.3/10.7	11.5 18.9
8 Mode D	1942	4	2×5900 16000	25 360/662	3800	3800	450	2C	4S	4S	6.8/5.9 11.2/9.7	5.3 8.7
9 Visby D	1943	4	2×13200 36000	26/350 360/662	3500	3000	450	2C	4S	4S	6.6/5.7 10.9/9.4	5.0 8.2
10 Tre Kronor CR	1947	2	2×33000 90000	33/375 465/707	3000	2800	250	2C	3S	2×6S	6.1/5.0 10.0/8.2	4.8 7.9
11 Öland D	1947	6	2×15000 40000	23/375 465/707	3800	2800	415	2C	4S	4S	6.1/5.0 10.0/8.2	4.8 7.9
12 Halland D	1955	2	2×21000 58000	41/450 580/840	3800	3250	370	1C+1S	4S	4S	5.8/4.7 9.5/5.7	4.3 7.1
13 Älvsborg ML	(1960)	(2)	1×9250 12600	36/450 465/840	9750	6500	325	1C+3S	5S	6S	4.6/4.1 7.6/6.7	<2 <3.3

D = destroyer
CR = cruiser
PB = patrol boat
M = minesweeper
ML = minelayer

The de Laval units were all single reduction cross-compound units with exception of the single-rotor designs for the small picket boats and minelayers with powers below 2 650 kW (3 600 shp) built before and during World War 2. The high pressure turbines had one or two Curtis stages for cruising and three to four single-stage impulse wheels for full power, figs 85, 86 and 87. The discs were shrunk on to the shaft with adjustable conical sleeves and axial keys to take the torque. The destroyers up to 'Öland' had one cruising steam admission valve and two bigger full power valves which were controlled by a hand wheel and a cam shaft. The full power nozzles were situated in the upper turbine casing. The steam from the cruising stages passed through the nozzles in the lower half. Dowel type couplings with bronze bushings were used. The experience with these simple coupling designs was excellent as long as they were supplied with sufficient lubricating oil. The shaft seals were made in halves with labyrinth-edges and relatively large clearances. The thrust bearings all had spherical support rings for the thrust pads. The bearing casings were bolted to the turbine casing with three radial centring keys.

The rotor speeds were more or less the same since 'Wrangel's 3 600 rev/min and had to be reduced for the engines of the cruisers 'Gotland' and 'Tre Kronor'. To achieve reasonable gear reduction ratios for the low propeller speeds in these ships, the speeds of the high pressure turbines had to be kept low. Steam pressures were low and only saturated steam was used before the 'Göteborg' of 1936, when Penhoet boilers with 26 bar, 350°C (360 lb/in², 662°F) were introduced in the Navy. With the 'Tre Kronor' and 'Öland', the steam conditions were somewhat raised, but first with 'Halland' of 1955 was the international 41 bar, 450°C (580 lb/in²/842°F) adopted. 'Tre Kronor' got hydraulically regulated nozzle valves, three on each side of the high pressure casing, fig. 86, four valves for ahead and two valves for astern. On 'Tre Kronor' manoeuvring was very conveniently performed. With one small hand wheel the ahead nozzle valves on the high pressure turbine were hydraulically actuated; with another, the astern valves were controlled.

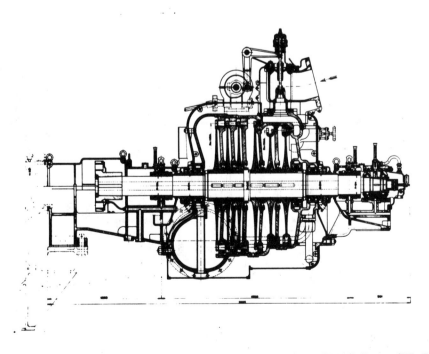

Fig. 85. High pressure turbine for the 'Göteborg' destroyer class of 1927. Power (HP+ LP) 9 500 kW (13 000 shp). Speeds 3 500/3 000/490 rev/min. Steam conditions 26 bar/ 350°C (360 lb/in²/662°F).

On the largest destroyer, 'Halland', de Laval returned to the simple mechanical cam-manoeuvred valves, according to fig. 87, with separate astern valves on the low pressure turbines.

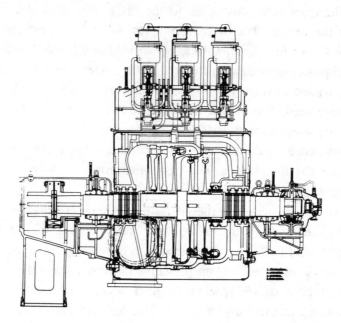

Fig. 86. High pressure turbine for the cruiser 'Tre Kronor' of 1957. Power (HP+LP) 33 000 kW (45 000 shp). Speeds 3 000/2 800/2 800/250 rev/min. Steam conditions 33 bar/375°C (465 lb/in²/705°F).

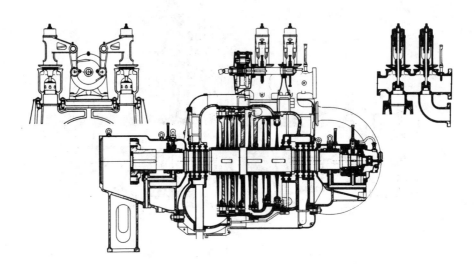

Fig. 87. High pressure turbine for the 'Halland' class destroyers of 1955. Power (HP+LP) 21 000 kW (29 000 shp). Speeds 3 800/3 250/370 rev/min.

For 'Tre Kronor' de Laval found that they could not use the traditional cross-compound arrangement as with only two pinions to take the torque, the bull wheel would have been too big for their 3 m (120 in) gear cutter. The designers chose an arrangement according to fig. 88 with two parallel low pressure turbines, one placed forward of the main gear, one aft. The low pressure pinions were placed on the same side and one above the other.

The low pressure turbines all had four impulse stages for ahead with the exception of 'Tre Kronor'. To split the pinion loading evenly, the heat drop in the high pressure turbine had to be reduced and the drop in the low pressure turbines increased. Therefore the high pressure rotor got only three impulse wheels and the low pressure rotors six each. The astern turbines consisted of one Curtis and one impulse wheel. On 'Tre Kronor' all nozzle chambers were welded in. No separate internal astern casings were used and no deflection vanes between the ahead and the astern exhaust blades. The low pressure steam from the auxiliaries was introduced into the low pressure ahead blading or was automatically discharged into the exhaust to the condenser. Designs are shown in fig. 89, 90 and 91. The exhaust blade speeds were increased from 'Wrangel's' 200 m/s to 'Halland's' 250 m/s. The rotor for the smaller units had speeds up to 3 800 and all others below 3 300 rev/ min.

The de Laval main gearings were all cut on the original hobbing machine of 1918 and were all single reductions. The 'Wrangel' gear was supplied with three-bearing pinions to take care of the high gear ratio (8:1) and the deflections of the slim pinions. With 'Ehrensköld' and a ratio of 7:1, normal two-bearing pinions could be used , as well as in the following destroyers up to 'Halland'. With the high reduction ratios for the cruisers 'Gotland' (8.4:1) and 'Tre Kronor' (12:1), as well as for 'Halland' (9.4:1), three-bearing pinions had to be used. A typical de Laval naval gear is shown in fig. 92 for the 'Halland' class destroyers of 1955.

To diminish the torsional deflection at the forward pinion teeth, the torque from the turbines was led through the hollow pinions to the coupling between the double bearing. The gear wheel was fabricated from thin steel castings and welded constructions. The gear rims were shrunk on to the bull wheel and secured by axial threaded dowel pins, half and half.

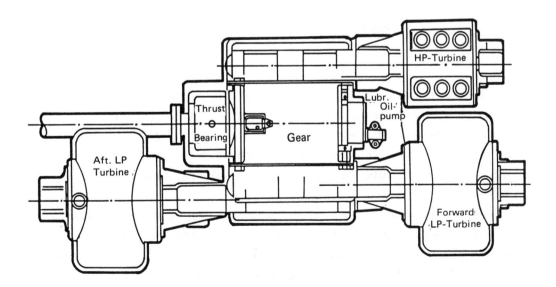

Fig. 88. Arrangement of the main turbines for the cruiser 'Tre Kronor' with two low pressure turbines 2 × 33 000 kW (90 000 shp).

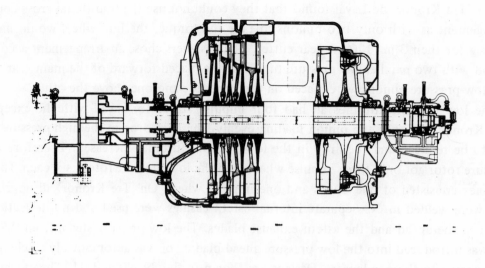

Fig. 89. Low pressure turbine for 'Göteborg'.

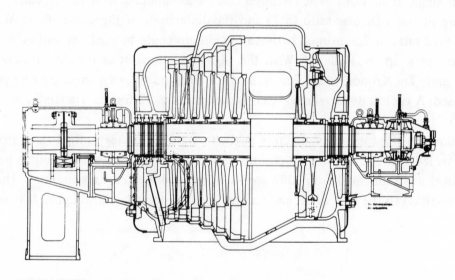

Fig. 90. Low pressure turbine for 'Tre Konor'.

The 'Velocimeter' was an old ingenious differential integrating revolution counter used to keep accurate distances between ships in close convoy duty — it was already installed in the first Swedish steam-engined destroyers early in the 1900's. Up to the 'Halland' class destroyers, pinion loadings were conservative and stayed in the range 5 to 6.2 bar (72 to 90 lb/in²). In the 'Halland' units, the Navy dared to go to more up to date values of about 9.4 bar (136 lb/in²).

The American development with double reduction gearing and solid rotors, which had been already introduced into the U.S. Navy during the thirties, cannot be traced in the Swedish developments until the design of the 'Älvsborg' in 1958. By then the age of steam in the Swedish Navy had already passed. Experience with the 'Älvsborg' designs could only be exploited in a few export deliveries and licensed manufacture for foreign navies, as the ship was cancelled in 1959.

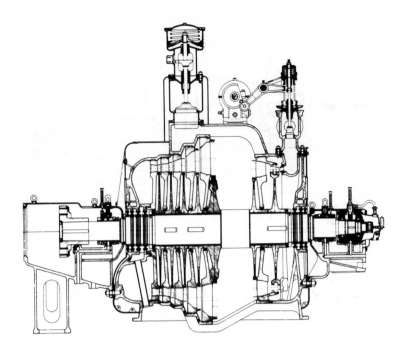

Fig. 91. Low pressure turbine for 'Halland'.

Over a period of 40 years steam consumptions were reduced by 40 per cent, and the weight a power ratio likewise. Weights in Table 16 include all auxiliary machinery with turbo-generators, condensers and pumps. As the amount of de Laval auxiliary machinery became more extensive over the years, this means that the weight of the main machinery was reduced by even more than the table shows. It is significant that the turbo-generators for the 'Wrangel' supplied 20 kW, those on the 'Göteborg' at first 40 kW and then 60 kW after a refit, while those on the 'Halland' were rated at 600 kW.

That the more important design details of de Laval machinery could be retained practically unchanged over such a long period of time, with a performance, in regard to weight, economy and availability, second to no other European turbine builder, is quite remarkable.

112

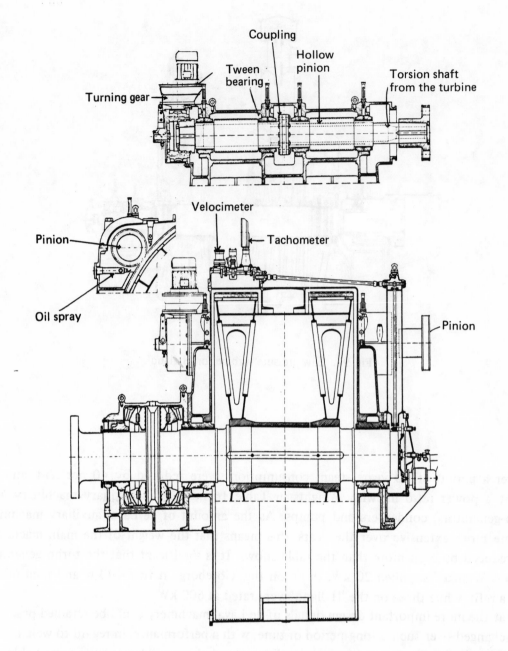

Fig. 92. Gearing for the 'Halland' class destroyers 21 000 kW (29 000 shp). Speeds 3 800/3 250/370 rev/min. Pinion with intermediate bearings and torsion shaft for mid-bearing coupling.

6.3 De Laval turbines in foreign warships

When that national pride of the French, the Blue Riband holder, 'Normandie', ran her trials in 1934, the turbo-generators were not accepted because of their quite unsatisfactory sound levels. The noise came from the six turbo-generators, each of 2.2 MW, supplied by the French company Alsthom. The turbine speed of 5 300 rev/min was geared down to 1 800 rev/min.

A noise analysis showed that the piercing, high frequency sound level was generated in the mesh because of tooth pitch errors made during machining of the rotating parts. To get rid of the noise problem, two test sets of gearing were ordered from the leading gear manufacturers of that time in Europe, de Lavals Ångturbin in Sweden and Maag in Switzerland. The de Laval gearing was the quieter, and that company finally made all six sets of gears. The result turned out quite satisfactorily, and the noise problem vanished.

This order is an indication of de Laval's know-how and reputation for gearing during the thirties. With such renown, it might well be thought possible for the company to build up a considerable export of high-quality gearing. In the absence of an effective sales organisation, however, and apart from a few random orders for special gears and smaller auxiliary turbines, there was never any significant export, despite the high quality of the products.

The first order outside of Sweden for a complete naval main machinery was placed in 1932 when the Norwegian Navy ordered a rather unusual combination propulsion plant for their minelayer, 'Olav Tryggvason'. For cruising powers, the ship had a diesel-electric unit of 2×520 kW (1 400 shp), with electric motors coupled directly to the propeller shafts. For higher speeds, single-casing geared steam turbines of the Swedish 'Jägaren' type were installed with an output of 2×1 700 kW (4 600 shp). At full speed, a total of 4 000 kW (5 500 shp) could be obtained from the two propeller shafts. The turbines ran at 3 730 rev/min, and were geared down to 310 rev/min on the propeller shafts. The steam pressure was the usual 19 bar (260 lb/in^2), and the boilers gave no superheat. 'Olav Tryggvason' gave peacetime service until the invasion of 1940, when the vessel fought at the Battle of Horten. The Germans appropriated the ship, which was later sunk during an Allied air-raid on Kiel towards the end of the war.

The next foreign order also came from Norway, in the shape of six turbine units for the 'Sleipner' destroyers. The ships were small coastal destroyers of 550 tons, powered with 2×4 400 kW, (12 000 shp). The turbines were principally scaled-down Swedish destroyer units.

They were completed during the period 1937 to 1941. 'Sleipner' fought in the battle for Norway and escaped to England when all her torpedoes and ammunition were used up. She became famous for her raids against the Germans, and remained in service until 1959, when she was scrapped. The other units were sunk or taken by the Germans.

Two destroyers were ordered in 1938 by Marinens Hovedverft, Horten, and given the numbers 129 and 130. These destroyers were comparatively large, about 1 000 tons, and were provided with the same turbines as the Swedish 'Göteborg' destroyers. They were almost complete when the Germans invaded the country in 1940. Despite great efforts, the Germans never succeeded in getting either of the ships in running order. The Norwegians continually sabotaged the work. After the war, some attempts were made to complete them and sell them for export but they were scrapped in 1960.

The Danish Navy became a customer of the Swedish de Laval Company in 1939 with orders for the destroyers 'Huitfeldt' and 'Willemoes'. Because of wartime conditions, work with the ships did not proceed very far, and the first trials were not carried out until 1947.

The destroyers were typical pre-war designs, and their turbines were, by and large, scaled-down versions of the Swedish destroyers of the thirties.

An important international order was placed with de Lavals Ångturbin in 1948 by the Jugoslavian Navy. Four complete destroyer units of the 'Göteborg' design were ordered, including all auxiliary machinery, under very favourable conditions for the company. The first part of the Jugoslavian destroyer deal was characterized by the collaboration between Tito and Moscow. All forgings and steel castings were to be delivered by the Skoda steelworks in Czechoslovakia. The Russians were to foot the bill for Jugoslavia's naval rearmament.

Before long, however, Stalin and Tito fell out with each other, and Stalin refused to permit any deliveries from Skoda, although the material had already been completed during 1948 to 1949. Without material for the main components of the machinery, work could not begin at de Laval. An agreement was made in 1951 between Jugoslavia and the U.S.A. for completing two destroyers, their armament to be delivered from the US. As de Laval was quite overbooked at that time with orders from the Swedish Navy and tanker machinery for export, an agreement was made with the Jugoslavian Navy for manufacturing the machinery under licence by the Jugoturbina Company at Karlovac.

New steel castings, forgings and other material were purchased in Sweden, and manufacture was started in both Jugoslavia and Sweden. Blade-machining and gear-cutting was carried out in Sweden, while the remaining machining was done in Jugoslavia. No ships' hulls were built, however, and the U.S.A. never delivered any guns. Jugoslavia made repeated attempts at the end of the fifties and during the sixties to sell the turbine units.

The Norwegian Navy issued an enquiry in 1961 for turbine machinery for some frigates built to NATO specifications. They were five single-screw ships with engine powers of 14 700 kW (20 000 shp). In competition with British and German manufacturers, the newly-merged company of Stal-Laval Turbin AB offered machinery based upon the prototype developed in 1959–1960 for the Swedish Navy's 'Älvsborg', which had been cancelled.

Now, the turbine know-how gained by de Laval designers during the fifties was put to good purpose. The rotors were high speed, solid-forged and over-critical in line with American practice. The first critical speed was placed at 60 per cent of the maximum speed. After studies in depth of various cruising speed arrangements, de Laval's established interstage admission system was chosen for the high pressure turbine as the simplest and most economic. The cruising section had a Curtis wheel and three single stages. The full power section had five single stages, fig. 93. At cruising speeds, the steam was admitted through two manoeuvring valves with welded-in diffuser nozzles in the upper half casing. Two similar, but larger, full speed valves with separate diffusers admitted live steam to the full speed wheels. Speed was 8 700 rev/min.

The low pressure turbine was designed with a solid rotor, and a speed of 5 300 rev/min, fig 94. The upper half casing consisted of a light shell of welded plate. The inner casing, which withstood the steam pressure, was completely independent of the outer casing, whose only function was to withstand the pressure of the atmosphere against the vacuum inside. The design was very light compared with conventional turbines. The astern turbine consisted only of a single Curtis wheel.

The Norwegian destroyer gearings were of locked-train design, fig. 95. Tooth loading was about doubled, compared with previous destroyer machinery, to 17–18 bar (246–261 lb/in^2) for the high pressure pinion. Both wheels and pinions were made of high alloy chromium steel. The teeth were shaved in accord with American procedure, and the couplings were fine-tooth type, replacing de Laval's old dowel and bushing-type coupling.

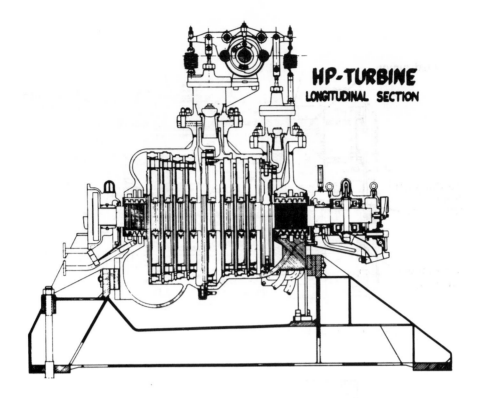

Fig. 93. Prototype drawing for the HP turbine for the 'Oslo' class destroyers. Steam cond. 36 bar (510 lb/in^2), 450°C (842°F). Power (HP+LP) 14 700 kW (20 000 shp). Speed 8 700 rev/min.

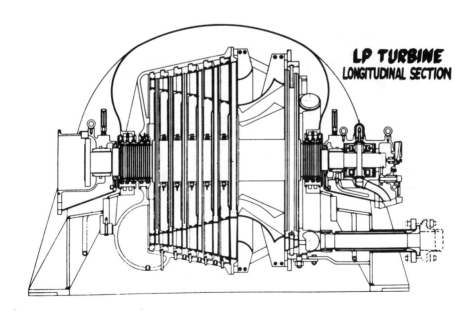

Fig. 94. Prototype drawing for the LP turbine for 'Oslo'. Speed 5 300 rev/min.

116

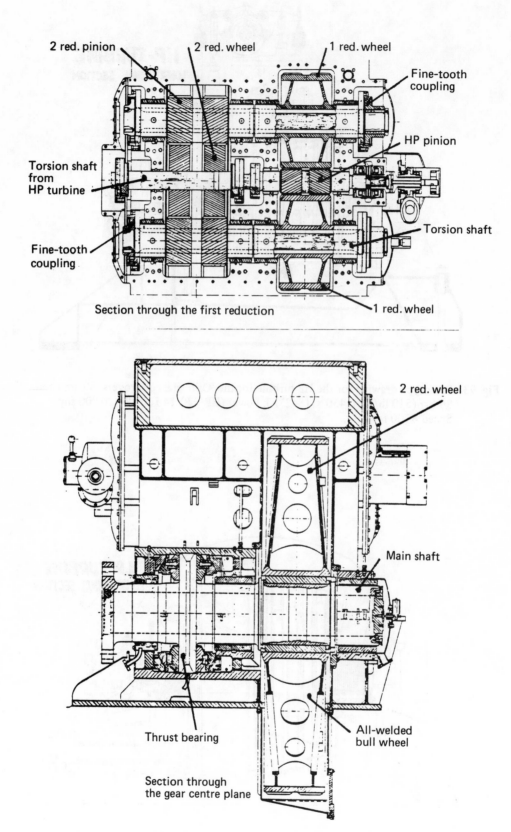

Fig. 95. Prototype drawing for the 'Oslo' gears. Power 14 700 kW (20 000 shp). Speeds 8 700/5 300/270.

The specific weight was halved compared with conventional single reduction units. The steam consumption was reduced by 10 to 15 per cent. Trials of the five 'Oslo' frigates took place from 1963 to 1965. Despite the newness of the designs, the turbines behaved without troubles.

The vessels were fairly large and seaworthy, and, as already mentioned, had only a single propeller shaft. Steam conditions were 41 bar, 450°C (580 (lb/in², 842°F), quite normal conditions for European frigates of that day.

The Italian licensees for tanker machinery, the shipyard Cantieri Navali Riuniti, signed an agreement in 1960 for naval turbines. By 1963 the large destroyer 'Impavido' ran her trials, followed by her sister ship 'Audace'. Using a draft design and calculations from Stal-Laval, Mr G. Satori at Cantieri Navali Riuniti, together with his engineers at Genoa, prepared a scaled-up version of the basic design from 'Älvsborg' and 'Oslo'.

Mr Satori had trouble getting the Italian naval administration to accept the over-critical rotors, and only when the U.S. Navy confirmed that such rotors had been standard for many years from American manufacturers, was the design approved. During trials on the 'Impavido', heavy vibrations occurred in the high pressure turbines.

At first, the over-critical rotor was blamed for the vibrations. When the turbine rotors were run uncoupled alone, however, they ran quite vibration-free.

The couplings were the next scapegoat. But it was found that the couplings centred themselves at quite a low torque, and were not thrown out to the limit of the clearance as had been feared. Finally, the long hollow shafting between the high pressure turbine and its pinion was investigated. To avoid a critical speed in these shafts, they had been made very light and thin. It was found that they had not been bored out absolutely concentrically, and deflected at higher speeds because of unbalance. After the couplings and quill shafts had been balanced at full speed, the vibrations disappeared. 'Impavido' was followed by a cruiser machinery of 2×22 000 kW (60 000 shp) for the 'Andrea Doria', who ran her trials in 1964. Finally, another destroyer machinery was built of 2×27 000 kW (75 000 shp) for the 'Audace' with trials in 1972 (figs 96, 97). The Italian designers followed closely the de Laval origi-

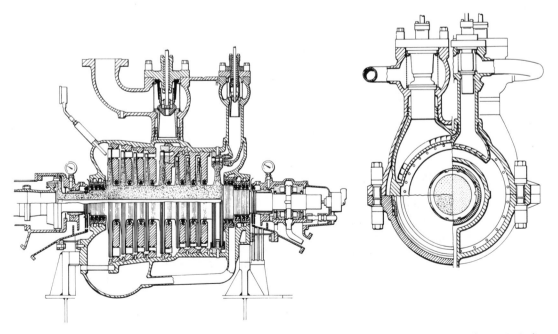

Fig. 96. HP turbine for the 'Audace'. Speed 7 600 rev/min. Power (HP+LP) 27 000 kW (36 500 shp). Steam conditions 46 bar, 440°C (653 lb/in², 824°F).

nal design, despite the tripled output. These units were regarded at that time as having record-low weights and at the same time good efficiencies. In Table 17, the main data for the de Laval machinery used by foreign navies has been summarized.

Table 17.

De Laval machinery in foreign navies

Ship	O=order T=trial Year	No. of ships	Output kW shp	Steam cond. bar/°C lb/in²/°F	Speed rev/min. HP	LP	Prop	Turbine arr. No. of impulse wheels HP Cruis./full speed	LP	Steam cons. full speed kg/kWh lb/shph
1 Olav Tryggvason Norway S	1934 T	1	2×1700 4600	19/sat 260 sat	3730		310	1C/1C+6S		7.5 12.3
2 Sleipner Norway D	1937 T	6	2×1900 12000	19 sat 260 sat	3600	3600	400	2C 4S	4S	6.8 11.2
3 MHV 129, 130 Norway D	1938 O	2	2×11000 30000	26/325° 360/622	3500	3000	475	2C 4S	4S	5.2 8.5
4 Huitfeldt Denmark D	1947 T	2	2×9000 24000	20/320° 276/608	3600	3250	435	2C 1C+2S	5S	5.2 8.5
5 Jugoslavia D	1947 O	4	2×11000 30000	26/350° 360/662	3500	3000	490	2C 4S	4S	5.2 8.5
6 Colombia D	1955 T	2	2×22000 60000	35/400° 480/752	3800	3250	370	2C 4S	4S	4.7 7.7
7 Oslo Norway F	1963 T	5	1×14700 20000	41/450° 580/842	8700	5300	270	C+3S 5S	7S	4.2 6.9
8 Impavido Italy D	1963 T	1	2×26000 70000	46/440° 653/824	7500	4500	360	C+3S 5S	7S	4.2 6.9
9 Andrea Doria Italy CR	1964 T	1	2×22000 60000	46/440° 653/824	7000	4300	340	C+3S 5S	7S	4.2 6.9
10 Audace Italy D	1972 T	1	2×27000 76000	46/440° 653/824	7600	4600	365	C+3S 5S	7S	4.1 6.7

D = destroyer
CR = cruisier
S = special ship
F = frigate

C = Curtis S = single

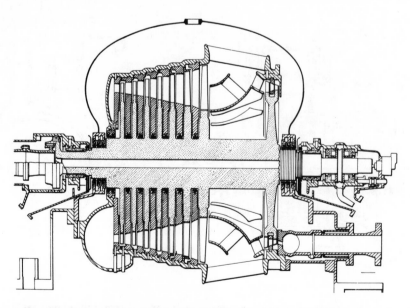

Fig. 97. Low pressure turbine for the 'Audace'. Speed 4 600 rev/min.

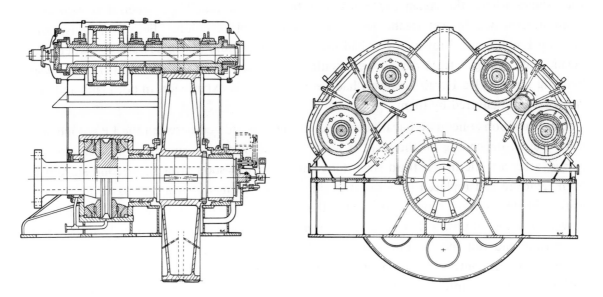

Fig. 98. The gearing for 'Andrea Doria'. Power 22 000 kW, speeds 7 000/4 300/340 rev/min.

If one makes an international assessment of the development of de Laval's naval turbines, one has to praise the pioneer work, which started with the 'Wrangel' turbines in 1918, and which successively went forward and improved. Admittedly, the gearing design was based upon American patterns through technology exchange with the Trenton company. But during more than 40 years, the little Swedish company managed to keep its naval turbine deliveries at the highest European levels, even if they fell short of the best American standards.

Compared with the developments initiated during the late thirties by the US Navy and carried out by the General Electric, Westinghouse and de Laval Trenton companies, the designs from European manufacturers stagnated, and here de Lavals Ångturbin was no exception.

American advances, such as the use of higher steam conditions, solid over-critical rotors and higher turbine speeds, combined with new designs for gearing using shaved, all-welded wheels, was not adopted by de Lavals Ångturbin until the sixties. By then, the epoch of steam power was already nearing the end for many types of warships. On larger warships, gas turbine power, with or without associated diesel engines for cruising speeds, took over.

6.4 The 'Great Blade and Disc Flutter' at de Laval Steam Turbine Co, 1944–1954.

As is evident from the preceeding section, the Swedish Navy regarded de Laval turbines as absolutely reliable and foolproof. There was some surprise, therefore, when reports came in that the low pressure turbines on the coastal destroyer 'Munin' were vibrating only some months after commissioning. An inspection revealed that several blades had broken off at the root. At first, faulty material was blamed, or faulty machining of a few blades.

New blades were fitted, but after a short period in operation the blades failed again. The failures occurred in the second stage of the LP turbine. The blades in that wheel had, if anything, lower stresses than the other low pressure stages. The fractures, therefore, seemed inexplicable. It was, however, common knowledge among the larger turbine manufacturers that stages where the steam expanded over the "Wilson Line", i.e. when it transformed from superheated to wet steam, were more prone to blade failures. Because of this, both General Electric and Brown Boveri had made it a design rule that blade stresses where the steam state changed from dry to wet should be designed to have about 25 per cent lower bending stresses. De Laval, however, had been spared this experience, in both land and marine turbines delivered by them.

The transition zone in de Laval's destroyer turbines wandered between the LP second and third stages, depending on the load. It was, therefore, not surprising that blade failure occurred after a while in the third stage too. This happened soon after the second stage had been removed and replaced by a distance ring. The problem stages in the coastal destroyers were rebladed several times, but mostly the turbines operated with some LP wheels removed. The loss of power that occurred by removing the wheels was surprisingly small, both at cruising and full speeds. But stranger still, one of the vessels, the 'Magne', never had a blade failure, in contrast to the other three vessels. The coastal destroyer problem remained without a solution into the fifties. Attempts made to strengthen the blade roots were unsuccessful. Operating time between failures became, if anything, less, and failures occurred even if the destroyers never went above three-quarters of the full speed power.

After trials on the 'Öland' and 'Uppland' during 1947 to 1948, fatigue cracks had been found, together with a few blade fractures of the same type that occurred in the second stage of the coastal destroyer LP turbines. New discs with reinforced blades were fitted on the 'Öland', but, as with the coastal destroyers, to no avail. The destroyers sailed, therefore, without a second stage in the LP turbines. In their case too, the fall-off in economy and speed was surprisingly small.

When the author started work at de Lavals Ångturbin in 1950, a few blade failures had also occurred in the third stage of the 'Öland' LP turbines. The Navy's patience had run out! The company received what amounted to an ultimatum to solve the problem. Investigations were started in three main areas. Failure could be due to:

1. Turbine discs and blades vibrating in some kind of resonance with axially combined blade and disc vibrations.
2. Metallurgical instability of the blade material and sensitivity to corrosion fatigue.
3. Moving blades vibrating in tangential resonance initiated by the diaphragm guide vanes and their vortex wakes.

Campbell's extraordinarily instructive theses, which dealt with General Electric's blade problems of 1924 and 1925, were studied intensively (see Part 1, p. 121 and bibliography). It was also found that no disc or blade vibration calculations had been made for many years. De Laval marine and land turbines had, however, despite the lack of vibration calculations, been almost free from blade failures during that period.

A whole series of comprehensive and instructive tests was begun. On the 'Öland', radial holes were drilled through the LP turbine casing opposite the second stage moving blades. On some of the blade platform tips, sharp chisel-shaped pins were screwed fast with the chisel edge in the plane of rotation. Small wooden pegs were inserted through the casing so as to make contact with the pins. If no blade or disc vibrations were present, the pins cut narrow, sharp grooves in the ends of the pegs during rotation. On the other hand, the pins cut relatively wide grooves if the blades were vibrating axially. The entire speed range was thus investigated, step by step. Judging from the grooves in the pegs, it became apparent that certain combined axial disc and blade vibrations were occurring with pronounced resonance at higher speeds.

At first, it was believed that the blade failures were due to these disc and blade vibrations that had been discovered. However, the vibration amplitudes at the blade tips were only about ± 1 to 1 1/2 mm according to the width of the grooves cut into the wooden pegs. There were no signs of dangerously large axial vibrations, for in such a case the platform tips would have contacted the guide vanes and wear marks would have been seen. Calculation checks showed that the stresses in the blade roots due to such small vibration amplitudes of ± 1.5 mm must be far below the fatigue limit.

The 'Öland' LP turbines were tested in a rig, and the discs were found to have resonances in the operating range. A new, stiffer LP disc was made and fitted, but the blade failure did not go away, fig. 99, in spite of the fact that no axial disc vibrations now occurred in the running range.

The second explanation of the blade failures was defects in the blading material. It was known from a couple of breakdowns on STAL's land turbines that stress corrosion and corrosion fatigue could seriously reduce the fatigue strength, even with the stainless 13 per cent chromium steel which was supposedly insensitive to such effects.

The main supplier of blading steel to de Laval was a smaller steel works, Vikmanshyttan. Complaints about supplies from Vikmanshyttan had been many. The specifications called for a carbon content of 0.2 per cent. Up to 50 per cent of the deliveries had to be scrapped due to slag inclusions and unacceptable metallurgical structure. To avoid these rejections, the steel works had raised the carbon content to 0.3 per cent without it being noticed by the customer. Continental steel works knew that higher carbon contents gave reduced fatique strengths, especially in the prescence of chloride ions (common salt). The increased carbon content gave a hard material with higher ultimate strength and yield point.

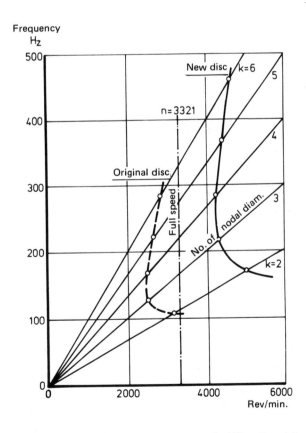

Fig. 99. Campbell diagram for the LP stage 2 disc on the 'Öland', original and strengthened.

122

To elucidate the sensitivity of the blade steel to corrosion fatigue in steam containing large amounts of chlorides, a number of comparative tests were made on various qualities of blade material. Chlorides in the turbine steam could be caused by priming of salt from the boiler drums. Boiler water often had high salt contents due to leakage of seawater into the condensers. A number of test pieces made from Vikmanshyttan's blading steel were subjected to bending fatigue in air, and in distilled water and water containing salt. A tangible result was obtained, fig. 100.

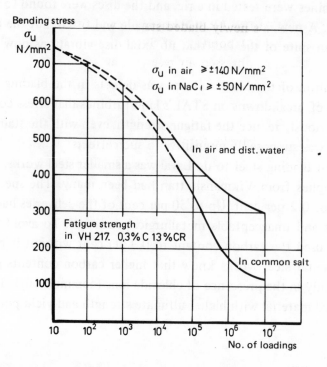

Fig. 100. Fatigue tests on rotating test pieces in air, distilled water and salt water. Vikmanshyttan's blade material with 0.3 per cent C.

The tests showed that Vikmanshyttan material was extremely sensitive to corrosion. The fatigue strength dropped from ± 140 N/mm^2 to about ± 50 N/mm^2 in the presence of chloride ions. A normal blade steel from Sandvikens Jernverk showed a reduction in fatigue strength of only 20–30 per cent in salt water. Sandviken did an investigation to produce a suitable blade material with a high fatigue strength in wet steam containing chlorides, and arrived at a quality with 13 % Cr, 0.5 % Mo, and 0.2 % C which gave very good test values. This material became the standard for all the company's blading, as it also had good strength at elevated temperatures.

Despite the low fatigue strength of the blade materials used, the blade failures were still unexplained. The calculated stresses in the blade roots were so small that failure seemed impossible, even taking account of the depressed fatigue strength in wet, salty steam. To clarify the vibration characteristics, a new, strengthened stage 2 wheel was made for the 'Öland' with reinforced blade roots.

This was sent to STAL's vibration laboratory at Finspong for rotation tests up to the highest speeds. In the spin chamber under vacuum, electromagnets were placed to give adjustable disturbing frequencies which could act upon the blades and discs. It was found for the new wheel that all resonant axial vibrations, both in the discs and the blades, were outside the running range, as shown by fig. 99. No tangential vibrations in the blades could be measured. The test equipment did indicate, however, very small and local forces on the blades in the tangential direction.

Tangential resonant vibrations could not, therefore, be eliminated, despite the spin chamber tests. As neither axial vibrations nor sensitivity to corrosion were the main culprits, the stresses on the blades during actual operation must in some way be determined. Placing strain gauges on blades working in steam was not yet possible. This technique was not to come for many years later. It was, however, of vital importance for de Laval quickly to find out what was the cause of all their blading troubles. It was therefore decided to make a single stage air turbine using Öland's newly bladed stage 2 wheel and the diaphragm belonging to it. This turbine was sent to the laboratory of Swedish Flygmotor and connected to that company's large, underground compressed air reservoir at Trollhättan. The test turbine was coupled to a hydraulic brake. The blades were fitted with strain gauges to measure all static and pulsating stresses. Jet engine technology had made many break-throughs with the use of strain gauges for measuring blading stresses in jet engine compressors and gas turbines.

By varying the air pressure and brake torque, the entire speed range could be tested with the pressures and torques which actually existed onboard ship. Using strain gauges and an oscilloscope, the amplitudes and stresses could be read and recorded. The Trollhättan tests gave an immediate answer to where the culprit was to be found. It became obvious that the guide vane vortices were causing tangential blade vibrations at the resonant frequencies of the blades.

It was found that at about 70 per cent full speed – corresponding to maximum speed on one boiler – powerful vibration peaks gave a clear-cut explanation to the blade failures in combination with unsuitable blading material. Three types of tip constraint between the blades were tested, fig. 101. The alternative with fixed ends was obtained by welding the tip platforms together. The gap between the tips was sawn open to get the free ends. The condition of the guided end was achieved by checking that the blade being measured was fitted without clearance and with no press fit. It was found that the disc and blades, as originally made, vibrated very closely to the 'fixed ends' alternative. For completely free blades, speed multiples of 6 to 16 vibrations per revolution appeared and gave high tangential amplitudes and stresses. On the original wheel, stresses of up to ± 80 N/mm^2 were measured.

Thus, the entire problem was solved, fig. 102. Blade failure was caused by the stresses from tangential vibrations combined with the depressed fatigue strength. The cure for the blading sickness in the LP turbines comprised three steps:

1. Lacing wire was fitted in all longer blades. The wires were loose in the holes in the blades, fig. 103. Tests showed that this reduced stresses from blade tangential vibrations by a factor of 10.
2. New, improved blade material with 0.5 per cent molybdenum, insensitive to corrosion fatigue, was used from then on.
3. Stiffer turbine discs with Campbell curves outside the operating range were made a design rule. For low pressure discs with long blades, the discs and blades were prescribed so stiff that resonance was impossible for excitation frequencies lower than 3.5–4 times the rotating speed.

Even if the problems in the destroyer LP turbines were cleared up after a while, blade problems were far from disposed of. It was now no longer low pressure blading, but the blades in the governing wheel. These blades are short, and therefore have insignificant stresses from centrifugal forces. But they have very large bending stresses caused by the steam jets issuing from the inlet nozzles. As a blade moves through the nozzle steam jet, the bending stresses vary from 0 to a maximum value.

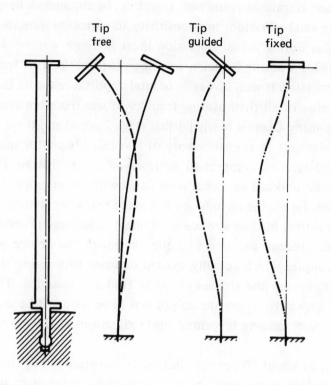

Fig. 101. Basic vibration forms for blades with free, guided and fixed ends.

A period of blading failure on Curtis wheels for main and auxiliary turbines appeared at the beginning of 1954. Blades started to fail in Curtis wheels and single stage governing wheels, for both land and marine turbines, even though the calculated stresses, based upon previous experience, were not exceeded. The individual blades in de Laval's design were not connected by shrouding. The tip platforms were held together by being assembled with a certain press fit. It appeared, however, that the tips could become free so that at high peripheral speeds and with heavy steam forces the blades could vibrate tangentially. The short blades had high natural frequencies which could be in resonance with the vortex wakes of the inlet nozzle guide vanes. With a free tip, the amplitudes easily became so large that far too high stresses occurred in the blade roots, with cracks or fracture as a consequence. There were a number of indications that the traditional de Laval root was not strong enough to cope with the bending stresses at high steam pressures and high peripheral speeds. Beginning in 1955 break-downs were reported from naval turbines and from the first tanker machinery.

After a serious blade failure in 1955 on the Curtis wheel of the tanker 'Saxon Sky', it was debated whether the de Laval blade root could be retained for the high pressures and high peripheral speeds expected for the new turbine types. The alternative, suggested by the customers, was to change to the international T–root with riveted shrouding. As early as 1950, designers at de Laval Trenton had said they were compelled to relinquish the de Laval root because of a series of blade failures. Up to moderate steam pressures and peripheral speeds, the root had functioned well, but with the introduction of more advanced steam conditions, severe blade troubles had appeared. The U.S. Navy had already condemned the de Laval root at the end of the thirties, and only T–roots and blades with riveted shrouding met their approval.

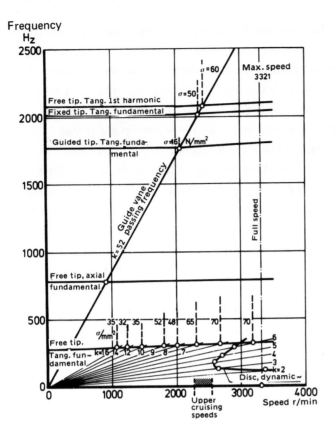

Fig. 102.

Results of the Trollhättan tests using strain gauges on an air turbine having 'Öland's' original stage 2 wheel, with free, guided and fixed blade ends.

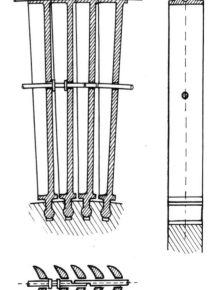

Fig. 103.

LP blade with tip-wire and lacing wire.

During an evening discussion at the Swedish de Laval, when the problem with the blade failures was being debated among the leading designers, one of the land turbine engineers announced that he had avoided blade failures in a governing stage by running a bead of weld metal along the blade tip periphery. This tied the blades together to a compact package. The method, however, was only a short-term solution as the weld bead cracked after a while, the cracks starting at the contact surfaces between the blade tip platforms.

The company was faced with a difficult choice. Changing to the international T-root was only a solution for future turbines, not for those already in operation. A cure for the blade problem in existing turbines was necessary if the company was to survive. The economic picture was not too good, but in no way could be compared with the situation that General Electric found themselves in during the twenties, when that company was involved with their great 'blade and disc flutter' period.

The destroyer investigations and the Trollhättan tests with lacing wires had shown how to retain the de Laval root for long blades, but for governing stages a solution must also be found. During the discussion that evening among the turbine designers, the solution appeared — the rolled-in tip wire, fig. 104. The simple modification saved the de Laval root, the company's reputation and future. Single and double tip-wires were introduced first in all governing stages. Thereafter, the modification was found to cost so little that it was used for all blading stages having a platform tip.

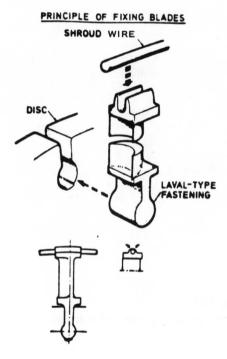

PRINCIPLE OF FIXING BLADES

SHROUD WIRE

DISC

LAVAL-TYPE FASTENING

Fig. 104.

Solution for blades with high bending stresses — the rolled-in tip wire.

Today, it is still the company's basic design for side-entry blading with platform tips. Only with extremely high steam pressures and stresses have they been forced to weld together blade packages of two or more blades, and use side-entry christmas-tree fastenings. Lately, electron-beam welding has been used to fasten the blade tip platforms together and the blades to the turbine discs.

The lengthy period of reports of blade failures was a nightmare. The author thought often of the situation General Electric had found themselves in with 500 turbine discs in operation, all shown by the Campbell diagrams to have natural frequencies within the running range. The problem for General Electric, however, was simpler as most of those turbines were constant speed machines. But for all those involved, it was a hard, even though instructive, lesson in vibration technology. Using experience from the Trollhättan tests, de Lavals Ångturbin quickly built up their own facility for vibration measurement in blades and discs. This provided invaluable material for calculating blade vibrations and vibration stresses.

7. THE FASTEST, BIGGEST, AND THE LAST ON THE NORTH ATLANTIC RUN

7.1 Lusitania and Mauretania

During the end of the 1890's and the beginning of the 1900's, the large German shipping companies, the Norddeutsche Lloyd and the Hamburg Amerika Line, took an increasing share of the North Atlantic traffic from their competitors, both with European emigrants as well as ordinary passengers. The giant liners, 'Kaiser Wilhelm der Grosse', 'Deutschland' and 'Kronprinz Wilhelm', initiated a ten year period when the speed record for the North Atlantic crossing was successively increased. The ships were from 14 000 to 17 000 BRT* and maintained regular traffic from 1897 across the Atlantic with record speeds of between 21 and 23 knots. With the 'Kaiser Wilhelm II' of 19 400 BRT, the Germans underlined their leadership by raising the record to 23.6 knots. These ships had powers of up to $2 \times 15\,000$ kW (40 000 shp) and had five or six cylinder quadruple expansion engines of enormous dimensions. The low pressure cylinders had diameters of more than 2 metres (6 ft). Speeds were low, from 75 to 80 rev/min.

This sustained German encroachment on the Atlantic route was a great setback for the world-famous British shipping companies of the Cunard and White Star Lines. With only a few lapses, they had previously held the Blue Riband ever since the Cunard ship, 'Britania', won it in 1840. This paddle steamer had crossed the Atlantic from Liverpool to Canada in twelve and a half days with a speed of 8 1/2 knots! Cunard was regarded by the majority of discerning travellers to be the best line on the Atlantic during the 1800's, with White Star as a good second. The level of the competition on the North Atlantic run at the beginning of the 1900's grew so serious for the British shipping companies that it became a Government matter to see that Britain regained her dominant position upon the Atlantic route. In 1903, the Cunard Line was granted by Act of Parliament a large, low-interest loan to build two record-large ships. The Admiralty also backed the plan as they saw the value of large, fast passenger ships, that could be quickly modified to troop transports in times of crisis. The two sister ships, 'Lusitania' and 'Mauritania', were ordered in 1904. They were launched in 1906, and entered service in 1907. Compared with the 19 400 BRT of the then current Blue Riband holder, 'Kaiser Wilhelm II', their tonnage had increased to almost 32 000 BRT.

The target was to give these leviathans a speed at least one knot higher than the liners being built by the German competition. This meant that the average speed across the Atlantic should at least be 24 1/2 knots. Already, the unit powers of up to 15 000 kW (20 000 shp) that the Germans were using in their ships had produced enormous, heavy reciprocating steam engines that were gluttons for steam. It was thought hardly likely that, these mastodons could be even further scaled up.

The Cunard management had followed with interest the advances of Charles Parsons with his marine turbines. A number of smaller units were in operation and had given good results. At the time of placing the order in 1906, there was only experience from a number of warships and a few cross-Channel steamers with powers up to 4 400 kW (6 000 shp). Two passenger ships, the 'Victoria' and the 'Virginia', were ordered in 1904 for the Allen Line, and had gone into service in 1905. They gave extraordinarily good results. But to go from Victoria's

*BRT = Brutto registered tons – a volume unit = 2.83 m³.
For passenger ships this represented approximately 1.15 displacement tons.

3×3 000 kW (12 000 shp) up to the powers specified for the new ships meant an extrapolation seldom met with in technology. Tank tests and calculations by the shipyard showed that engine powers above 45 000 kW (60 000 shp) were necessary to produce the speeds demanded.

The competing German ships all had only two propellers, but this arrangement was not practical with turbine operation. Parsons had to divide the power over four shafts. During trials, it was proven that 4×13 600 kW (73 000 shp) could be got out of the machinery, which is described in Part 1, page 26. The main data for the 'Mauritania' and 'Lusitania' are summarized in Table 18 and compared with later large and fast passenger liners on the North Atlantic run. 'Mauritania', fig. 105, won the Blue Riband in 1907 and kept it without difficulty for 22 years, until the German 'Bremen', twice as big and almost twice as powerful, took the trophy.

Fig. 105. 'Mauritania' in 1907. 31 500 BRT, 27.2 knots, 54 000 kW (73 000 shp).
'Turbinia' from 1897, 44 tons, 34.5 knots, 1 500 kW (2 000 shp).

'Lusitania' was sunk by a German submarine in 1915. This event was one of the reasons for the U.S.A. entering the War in 1917. 'Mauritania' served as a troop transport during the First World War, and in 1919 could resume her voyaging between Southampton and New York. In 1921, the ship was modernized, and the boilers were converted to oil-firing. From 1930, the vessel was largely used for cruising. In 1935, she was deemed to have done her duty and sent to the scrapyard. Cunard built a second 'Mauritania' in 1939, but that vessel was built more for economy than prestige. The ship was of 35 700 BRT, and was given a power of 2×15 700 kW (42 000 shp) which could produce a speed of 23 knots. This liner was regarded as a comfortable and safe ship, but she never gained the prestige and fame of the original 'Mauritania'.

Table 18.

Queens of the North Atlantic

Ship	Lusitania Mauretania GB	Leviathan ex. Vater-land G (USA)	Bremen Europa G	Normandie F	Queen Mary Queen Elisabeth GB	United States USA	France F	QE2 GB
Deliv. year	1907	1911(1927)	1929/30	1935	1936/40	1952	1962	1969
Yard	John Brown Swan Hunter	Blohm & Voss	AG Weser Blohm & Voss	Penhoët	John Brown John Brown	Newport News	Atlan-tique	John Brown
Tonnage, BRT	31550/31940	54200	51660/49750	83430	81240/83670	53300	66300	65862
Length, m	241	290	287	314	314	302	315	294
Power, kW	54000	60000	100000	123100	120000	180000	120000	82000
shp	73000	80000	135000	165000	160000	240000	160000	110000
Norm/max speed km	26/27.2	22.5/24	27/28.5	29/32.2	29/32.3	24/35.5	31/33	28/29.5
No. of boilers	25	46	24	33	27 / 12	6	8	3
No. of props	4	4	4	4	4	4	4	2
Steam bar/°C	16/sat	17/sat	24/370°	28/350°	25/370°	61/540°	72/500°	60/510°
lb/in²/°F	217/sat	230/sat	330/700°	390/660°	350/700°	870/1000°	1030/932°	855/950°
Turbines	John Brown Swan Hunter	Blohm & Voss	Deschimag Blohm & Voss	Alsthom Zoelly	John Brown John Brown	Westing-house	CEM	John Brown Pametrada
Turbine type	Parsons	Parsons	Parsons	Impulse	Parsons	Impulse	Parsons	Impulse
Speed HP/LP	190/190	180/180	1800/1800 2480/1200	2430/2430	1530/1030	4750/4005	3044/2224	5207/3192
Prop. speed	190	180	180 218	243	180	188	156	174
Turb. arr.	2×HP/LP	LP/HP/ /SPHIP/ LP	G(HP+IP+LP) G(HP+IP+LP)	4TG(HP+LP) 4EM	G(HP+IP1+ IP2+LP)	GG(HP+LP)	G(HP + IP1+IP2+ LP)	GG(HP+LP)
Fuel cons. kg/shph	0.6	0.6	0.35	0.27	0.27	0.22	0.22	0.22
lb/shph	1.3	1.3	0.77	0.6	0.6	0.49	0.49	0.49

7.2   Leviathan ex. Vaterland

The German shipping line, Norddeutsche Lloyd, in no way gave up the fight to retain their position as the largest carrier of passengers across the North Atlantic. Experience from the 'Mauritania' and 'Lusitania' was assessed in great detail, and in 1909 a new, giant passenger liner was ordered from the famous Blohm & Voss yard in Hamburg. The ship was of record size, 54 200 BRT, fig. 106. It was found, however, that the cost of installing an engine power sufficient to compete with the speed of the Cunard ships would be much too great. The maximum power was thus limited to 4×15 000 kW (80 000 shp). The design of the turbines was based on material from Parsons together with experience from the Cunard ships' machinery. Propeller speed was reduced to 180 rev/min. Turbine dimensions were considerably larger than for the 'Lusitania' and 'Mauritania'. Normal speed was only 22 1/2 knots. It was the first time a large ship was fitted with water-tube boilers. They were almost twice as many as on the 'Mauritania' — a total of 46. To get good economy at cruising speeds, an interesting series-parallel arrangement was built, probably the first of its kind, fig. 107.

The two inboard shafts were coupled to the high pressure turbines, both for ahead and astern operation. The two outboard shafts had low pressure turbines, also for ahead and astern. At maximum speed, steam was supplied from the main nozzle valves 1 and 2 to the two high pressure turbines, the steam then passing to the low pressure turbines on the outboard shafts. The machinery on either side thus worked independently with a cross-compound arrangement. At cruising speeds, the port high pressure turbine received live steam from valve 1, but the exhaust to the port low pressure turbine was closed by valve 3. Instead, valve 4 was opened leading the steam to the combined high and intermediate pressure turbine, HIP. The exhaust steam was then led to both outboard shafts by opening valve 5. In this way, a considerable gain in steam economy was obtained. For astern operation, both propeller shafts on the two sides worked as separate units.

Fig. 106. 'Vaterland'/'Leviathan', 1911. 54 200 BRT, 24 knots, 60 000 kW (80 000 shp).

Vaterland Turbine Arrangement (1911)

For max. speed, valves 1, 2, 3 open, 4, 5 shut.
For cruising speeds, valves 1, 4, 5 open, 2, 3 shut.
For manoeuvring, valves 1, 3 alt. 2 open, 4, 5 shut.
For astern, valves 6 alt. 7 open, 1, 2 shut.

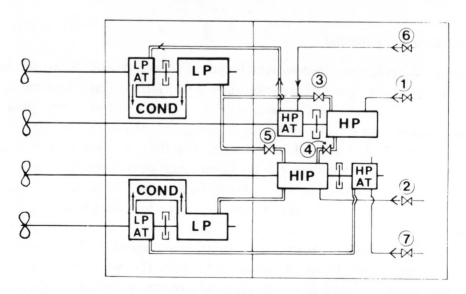

Fig. 107. Diagram of Vaterland's' series-parallel arrangement of high and intermediate pressure turbines. Arrangement: LP/HP/SPHIP/LP.

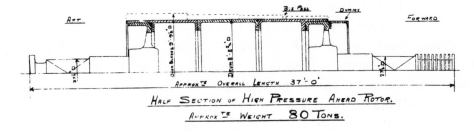

Section through Vaterland's high pressure turbine.

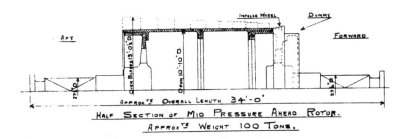

Section through Vaterland's intermediate pressure turbine.
Live steam admitted to the Curtis wheel during parallel operation.

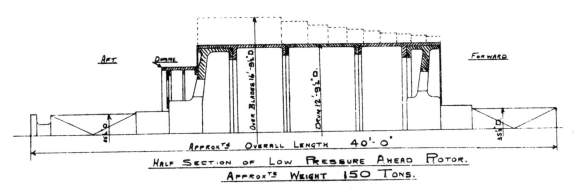

Section through one of Vaterland's low pressure turbines.

Fig. 108. Sections through Vaterland's direct-driving ahead turbines. Speed 180 rev/min. Impulse blading was used by Blohm & Voss to some extent. Curtis wheels in intermediate and astern turbines.

All four high pressure turbines could, in addition, be connected to the condensers by valves and piping, so that each shaft could be manoeuvred independently of the others. Steam could also be admitted to all four low pressure turbines. In all, the ship was manoeuvred with eight nozzle control valves, three change-over valves for series-parallel connection, and four extra valves for exhausting the high pressure turbines to the condensers. Fig. 108 shows sections through the ahead turbine rotors. The low pressure rotors had a diameter of over 5.1 metres, a length of 12.2 metres and a weight of 150 tons. (Corresponding values for the 'Mauretania' were 4.7 metres, 10 metres and 100 tons.)

When the First World War broke out, the 'Vaterland' was in an American harbour, and was annexed when the U.S. entered the war. The vessel served as a troopship for carrying American troops to Europe. She was renamed 'Leviathan', and played a large part in the vital transportation from the U.S. to Europe. In 1922, the ship was returned to her original duties, and earned a great reputation in the U.S. American Line. The famous ship designer, William Gibbs, was responsible for the refitting, and the ship became renowned for her extremely beautiful and practical furnishings. The vessel was also converted to oil-firing, and the stokehold crew could be reduced to a fraction of that previously necessary. She worked the North Atlantic route until 1938. After a while she became uneconomic because of fuel costs, for, like the 'Lusitania' and 'Mauretania', she was a glutton for coal and oil.

7.3 Bremen and Europa

Despite the hard times in Germany during the twenties, the large shipping lines of Norddeutsche Lloyd and the Hamburg Amerika Line decided to replace the 'Vaterland' and 'Deutschland' with new, modern ships, somewhat smaller than 'Vaterland', but with powers that would assure them a place among the Blue Riband winners. The two famous German yards, A.G. Weser and Blohm & Voss, received orders for the 'Bremen' and 'Europa' respectively in 1927. The specifications were by and large the same, but the vessels were different in many respects. Dr Gustaf Bauer, A.G. Weser's chief engineer in Bremen, and Dr Prahm of Blohm & Voss in Hamburg were world-famous shipbuilders and machinery designers. They designed their ships independently of each other, but to the same main specifications. Both A.G. Weser's engine builders, Deschimag, and Blohm & Voss were among the largest Parsons licensees.

Fig. 109. 'Bremen' from 1929. 51 660 BRT, 28.5 knots, 100 000 kW (135 000 shp).

The machinery power was almost double that of the 'Mauretania', namely 4 x 25 000 kW (135 000 shp), which gave a normal speed of 27 knots, and a maximum speed of about 28 1/2 knots. During the more than twenty years since the 'Mauretania' machinery was built, there had been developments in reduction gear technology, and the British battlecruiser 'Hood' had demonstrated that geared machinery could be built in power units up to 26 500 kW (36 000 shp). Dr Bauer and Deschimag decided to split the power over three turbine cylinders, each with its pinion driving through the gear. Steam pressure was 24 bar (330 lb/in^2) and the superheat temperature 370°C (700°F). The arrangement of the turbines is shown by fig. 110. The shipping company had asked for such a high astern power that two astern turbines were necessary, a Curtis wheel coupled to the intermediate pressure turbine and

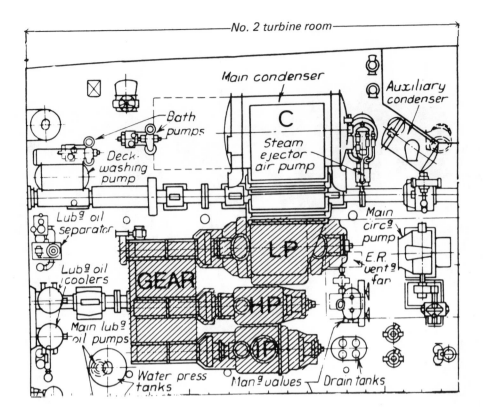

Fig. 110. Arrangement in one of 'Bremen's' four turbine rooms, with three turbine cylinders, and astern wheels in the intermediate and low pressure turbines.

a double-flow reaction section in the middle of the low pressure turbine. All turbine cylinders were disposed forward of the gear box, with the high pressure turbine pinion highest up on the gear wheel. The high pressure turbine had a Curtis wheel followed by a reaction drum. The speed was the same for all turbines, 1 800 rev/min, which was geared down to 180 rev/min at the propeller. The pinions were supported in three bearings, a necessity with reduction ratios of 1/10. Intermediate and low pressure turbine pinions were situated in the horizontal plane of the gearing. Fig. 111 shows the turbine unit on the test bed with the upper half casings lifted, and fig. 112 shows the low pressure rotor in the balancing machine. The space under the low pressure turbine was quite insufficient to accommodate a condenser. The condensers were therefore placed at the side of the low pressure turbines and connected by enormous exhaust steam pipes. This arrangement meant that the low pressure turbine had to be drained to a special drain tank situated low down. This had to be shut off periodically to enable the condensate to be sucked up into the condenser. With the large steam exhaust pipes and pipe connections to and from the ahead and astern portions of the intermediate pressure turbine, the arrangement was rather cramped, and must have given rise to many swear words and other comments when the turbines were to be opened for inspection, fig. 113.

The gear tooth loading was very conservative with K=5 bar (75 lb/in^2). Main wheel diameter was 4 metres (158 in). During the trials there were a few mishaps with blade failures in the high pressure turbine Curtis wheel. But after replacing these blades with stronger ones, the 'Bremen' displayed an extremely high availability, as did also her sister ship, 'Europa'.

'Europa's' turbines were designed by Blohm & Voss, and had a quite different arrangement, fig. 114. Here, the designer used only two pinions, had coupled the high and inter-

Fig. 111 'Bremen's' main turbine on the test bed, 25 000 kW (33 750 shp), 24 bar 370° (330 lb/in², 700°F), High pressure turbine pinion meshes at the top of the main gear wheel. Low pressure turbine hidden by high pressure turbine foundation. Turbine speed 1 800 rev/min, propeller 180 rev/min.

Fig. 112. 'Bremen's low pressure rotor in the balancing machine. The two astern reaction drums were situated at the centre of the rotor; the ahead blading steam flow was inwards from the outside. Speed 1 800 rev/min.

Fig. 113 'Bremen's' main turbine and gearing on the test bed with the water brake. Observe the extremely cramped arrangement with all the pipe connections.

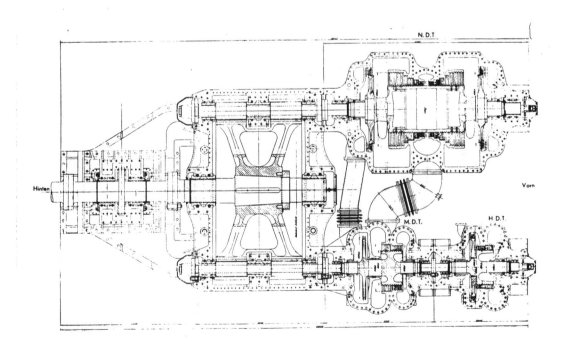

Fig. 114 'Europa's' main turbine and gearing. Arrangement $4 \times G(\overline{HP+IP}+LP)$. Turbine speeds 2 420 and 2 000 rev/min respectively, propeller speed 218 rev/min.

mediate turbines in tandem to one pinion, and the low pressure turbine to the other. Speeds were higher than for the 'Bremen'; 2 480 for the high and intermediate shafts and 2 000 rev/min for the low pressure shaft, reducing to 218 rev/min at the propeller. The arrangement was simple. An astern turbine consisting of a single Curtis wheel was placed at the aft end of the intermediate pressure turbine, thence the steam was led to two parallel Curtis wheels in the low pressure turbine. The gearing had hollow pinions supported in three bearings, and long torsion shafts connected by couplings at the after end. These were so calculated as not to give any torsional vibrations within the normal speed range.

The remarkable features of the 'Europa' turbines were the extremely short reaction drums in the high and intermediate pressure turbines, and the large Curtis wheel in the high pressure turbine. Also, because of the tandem arrangement, dummy pistons could be dispensed with. The design must be judged as elegant compared with what was being done by other reaction-type builders at that time.

'Bremen' won the Blue Riband in 1929 and kept it until the larger French liner, 'Normandie', went into service in 1935. 'Europa' too made a record run with a west-bound crossing in 1930, thus giving her a place in the Blue Riband Club. During the Second World War, 'Europa' was laid up in Bremen, and was handed over to France at the end of hostilities, whereafter she sailed as the 'Liberty' under French flag. 'Europa' was not scrapped until 1961. 'Bremen' was so damaged by fire during the war that she was never restored again but was sent to the scrapyard.

Fig. 115.   'Normandie' from 1935. 83 430 BRT, 32.2 knots, 123 100 kW (165 000 shp). Turbo-electric driven.

7.4 Normandie

The large French shipping line, Companie General Transatlantique, had maintained a regular traffic between French ports and the major ports in America and Canada since the middle of the 1800's. In 1912, the Penhöet yard at St. Nazaire built the 24 000 tonner, 'France', in 1922 the 'Paris' of 25 000 tons and the 44 000 tonner, 'Ile de France', in 1927. They all had four propellers and were fitted with direct-driving turbines. The power of the 'Ile de France' was $4 \times 12\,000$ kW (64 000 shp). Competition from the 'Bremen' and 'Europa' began to be felt, and the company found the time was ripe for building a new large passenger ship to run together with the 'Ile de France'. In spite of the reduced traffic over the Atlantic, and the recession of 1929, they decided, with the full backing of the French Government, to build an Atlantic liner that would show the world what French engineers and French naval architects could do. During the Depression, amid unemployment and other difficulties, the first keel plates for the 'Normandie' were laid in 1931.

At the same time as the keel was laid, towing tests were begun with various hull forms in the large tank at Hamburg. Relatively quickly, the lines began to emerge of a giant ship having a displacement of 67 500 tons and an overall length of 314 metres. Tests on self-propelled models, together with detail calculations, showed that the shipping line's demand for a speed in excess of 29 knots and a tonnage of over 80 000 BRT required a power of 118 000 kW (160 000 shp). Even with four propellers, the designers found that the unit power was so large that turbo-mechanical operation was inadvisable with regard to anticipated gear problems. The unit power was definitely much greater that that of the 'Hood', and in addition, this was to be for a passenger ship that would be using her full power almost continuously.

The U.S. Navy and the General Electric had demonstrated that considerably higher powers could be obtained with turbo-electric operation. At a very early stage, therefore, the company decided to use that form of propulsion. The French turbine firm of Alsthom made Zoelly turbines, and also had a cooperation agreement with General Electric, the world leader for turbo-electric operation.

The author worked at the St. Nazaire yard during the first tests of the machinery. 'Normandie' had exceedingly beautiful lines, fig. 115. The enormous space for passengers, with its luxurious and artistic decorations, provided memories for a lifetime. The devastating effect of unemployment on a small community such as St. Nazaire was also a long-lasting memory. The hull was designed by the famous Russian designer Yorkevitz, and the hull form anticipated the modern bulb-design with hollow lines at the waterplane. The tonnage of the 'Normandie' finally became 83 430 BRT.

Because of strikes and insufficient financing, the completion of the 'Normandie' was delayed. For almost two years hardly any work at all was carried out onboard, and not until 1935 was the vessel ready for her trials.

'Normandie's' machinery included an imposing boiler installation, consisting of 29 water-tube boilers and 4 Scotch boilers. Steam data were 28 bar, 350°C (390 lb/in², 660°F) not greatly different from the Bremen's' 24 bar, 370°. The boilers had air-preheaters. The propulsion machinery consisted of four turbo-generators, each with a high and low pressure turbine in tandem driving a generator. The turbines were placed fore-and-aft side by side in a turbine room. The turbines drove four-pole generators at 2 430 rev/min. Four large direct-driving forty-pole motors were placed in a motor room aft, driving the four propellers. Transmission was with 3-phase current at 5 500 volts. At full speed, the frequency was 81 cycles/second. When the motors were running synchronously, the speed reduction was 1/10, giving a propeller speed of 243 rev/min at full power. For a merchant ship, especially one of the size of the 'Normandie', this speed was extremely high, but the yard believed they had sufficient experience with warships at such high speeds and powers. The risks of vibrations from the propellers with attendant cavitation were underestimated, however. The propeller efficiency must have been considerably lower than for the 'Bremen' and the 'Europa', because of the appreciably higher rotational speed. Astern manoeuvring was easily accomplished by switching over two of the phases from the generators. Normally, each generator powered its own motor, and thus all manoeuvring could be very simply carried out. The electric motors had special windings for running as induction motors at lower powers. The generators were thus run at constant low speed when manoeuvring, and the propeller speed was controlled electrically, ahead and astern. At higher powers, the propeller motors ran synchronously with the turbo-generators until the required speed was obtained. The shop trials proved the machinery to run remarkably vibration-free, and the designers hoped that the ship would behave just as docilely and vibration-free when running at higher powers in spite of the high propeller speed.

The Alsthom turbo-generators had Zoelly-type impulse turbines, fig. 116. The generators were air-cooled with enclosed air circulation. The condensers were placed under the low pressure turbines in accordance with land practice. By and large, this part of the machinery was quite like a land power station.

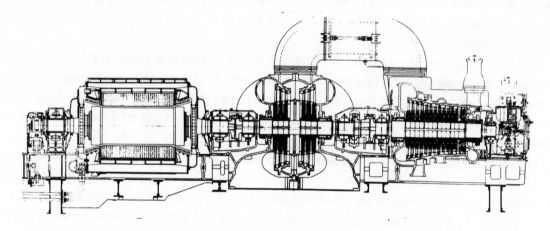

Fig. 116. Section through one of the turbo-generators on the 'Normandie', 28 bar, 350°C (390 lb/in^2, 660°F), 30 000 kW, 2 430 rev/min, 5 500 volts, 81 Hz.

During the trials of 1934–1935, however, very heavy hull vibrations occurred with resonances from the three-bladed propellers, with amplitudes which became very disagreeable at the stern, even at normal speeds. The ship made a number of passages across the Atlantic, and actually captured the Blue Riband with a speed of almost 32 knots with her original three-bladed propellers.

The vibrations, however, were so serious that redesigned four-bladed propellers were ordered as quickly as possible. With these new propellers, the ship became on a par with her competitors with regard to vibrations, but she was never really free from vibrations at top speeds. With present-day propeller technology, the 'Normandie' could certainly have been made practically vibration-free, for example, using five-bladed propellers with skewed blades.

The specific fuel consumption of the 'Normandie' was about the same as those of the 'Bremen' and the 'Europa', despite the higher losses encountered with the electrical transmission. On the other hand the actual specific fuel consumption, based upon ahead propulsive power, must have been worse due to the higher propeller speeds and the consequent lower propeller efficiency. The 'Normandie' did not keep her Blue Riband for long. Already in the autumn of 1936, the 'Queen Mary', with a few tenths of a knot to spare, managed to beat the 'Normandie's' record speed. In 1937, the 'Normandie' retook the speed record with almost 31 knots, but the 'Queen Mary' took the lead again in 1938. The difference in time between these two ships on the Atlantic run was equivalent to only some tenths of a knot. The 'Normandie' was comparatively well-booked up until the outbreak of the Second World War, and her machinery behaved faultlessly. When the Germans invaded France, the 'Normandie' remained in New York. She was taken over by the U.S. government when they later entered the war. The intention was to refit her for transporting troops. Fire broke out onboard, however, during the rebuilding. Through unusual bungling by the New York fire department, so much water was pumped into the upper decks to extinguish the blaze that she capsized and sank, even though she was moored to the quay.

Nobody knowledgeable in ship stability and marine matters was present, either from the new owners or the old, nor had anybody authority to act. The U.S. Navy raised her after a few years, but the destruction was so great that there was nothing else to do but send this wonderful engineering and architectural masterpiece to the scrapyard.

7.5 'Queen Mary' and 'Queen Elizabeth'

The German ships, 'Bremen' and 'Europa', meant to a considerable setback for Cunard passenger fleet on the Atlantic route. A number of smaller ships had certainly been built, but by the end of the twenties a replacement for the 'Mauretania' was seen as a clear necessity, for both economic and prestige reasons. Despite the 1929 stock market crisis in America and the consequent reduction in the North Atlantic traffic, Cunard decided to build a new passenger liner. This ship was to be of such excellence as to defend the British colours not only against her two German competitors, but also against the then newly decreed French contender, the 'Normandie'. The first keel plate was laid in 1930, but already by 1931 all design work and building at John Brown's yard were discontinued. The economic situation in Great Britain was such that no way of completing the ship could be seen due to financial difficulties. In 1934, however, Cunard and the White Star Line were amalgamated to a single company. This put sufficient capital at the disposition of the new shipping line to enable work to be resumed on the 'Queen Mary'. In many respects, the ship became more conventional than the 'Bremen', 'Europa' and the 'Normandie'. The tonnage was somewhat lower than the 'Normandie's, at 81 240 BRT, fig. 117. The official machinery power was about the same as that of the 'Normandie', i.e. 4 × 30 000 kW (160 000 shp). The ship was given three funnels for her 27 water tube boilers. Her lines were conventional and there was no bulb at the bows.

Steam data was 25 bar, 370°C (350 lb/in², 700°F), which were also conventional values, practically the same as for her seven year older German adversaries. In contrast to the French turbine designers, John Brown and Parsons had no qualms in choosing turbo-mechanical propulsion, even with unit powers of 30 000 kW (40 000 shp). A four cylinder arrangement was chosen, High pressure and first intermediate pressure turbines were placed

Fig. 117. R.M.S. 'Queen Mary' from 1936. 81 240 BRT, 32 knots, 120 000 kW (160 000 shp).

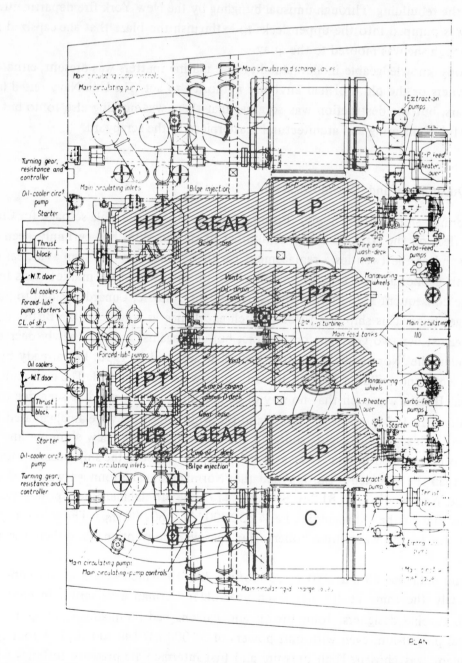

Fig. 118. After turbine room on the 'Queen Mary'. Machinery arrangement 4 × G(HP+IP1+IP2+LP)

aft of the gearing, while the second intermediate and low pressure turbines were put forward of the gearing, see fig. 118.

The high pressure and first intermediate pressure turbine pinions were placed in elevated positions on the gear, while the other two turbine pinions were placed in the plane of the gearing horizontal joint. With this arrangement, the low pressure turbine was located so low that its exhaust was directed upwards and to the side to reach the condenser. Thus, here too the condensers lay above the low pressure turbines. The design engineers chose a propeller speed of 180 rev/min.

The traditional Parsons designs with large reaction drums and low speeds were a characteristic of Queen Mary's high and first intermediare pressure turbines. The second intermediate

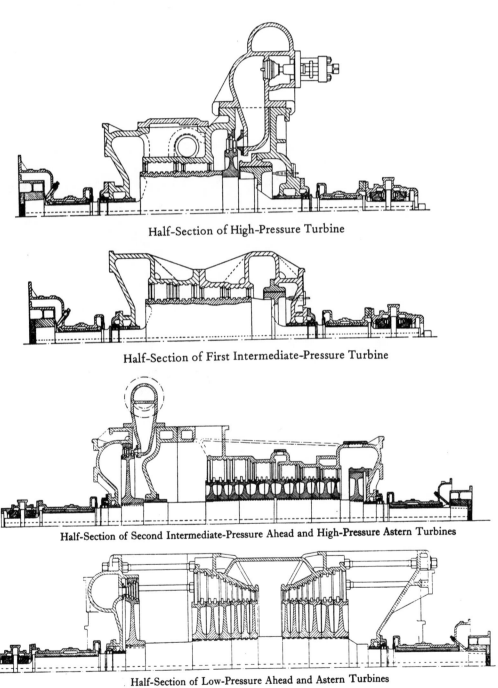

Half-Section of High-Pressure Turbine

Half-Section of First Intermediate-Pressure Turbine

Half-Section of Second Intermediate-Pressure Ahead and High-Pressure Astern Turbines

Half-Section of Low-Pressure Ahead and Astern Turbines

Fig. 119. Sections through 'Queen Mary's' high, intermediate and low pressure turbines.

and low pressure turbines had rotors with shrunk-on discs. To get acceptable tooth loadings at the high power, very low speeds were chosen for the turbines — 1 530 rev/min for the after turbines, and 1 030 rev/min for the forward turbines, including the low pressure turbines. The high pressure turbine had a Curtis wheel. In general, the blading was of the traditional Parsons type. The second intermediate and low pressure turbines had astern turbines.

The appearance of the turbine unit can be seen from fig. 120. The main gear wheel was made of cast iron, a bolted design with shrunk-on gear rims. To avoid torsional vibrations, the pinions were bored out and had torsion shafts coupled to the pinion dog couplings. The pinions were supported in three bearings despite the low reduction ratios. The gear casing was cast iron, and had an integral thrust bearing. Gear loadings were low, K=5.5 bar (80 lb/in^2). The steam control system was simple, and used four governing valves with nozzle groups in the high pressure turbines. The second intermediate pressure turbine had three astern nozzle groups controlled by governing valves.

Fig. 120. Photo of 'Queen Mary's' main turbines on the workshop test bed. 25 bar, 370°C (350 lb/in^2, 700°F), 30 000 kW (40 000 shp), 1 530/1 530/1 030/1 030/180 rev/min.

The 'Queen Mary' and the 'Normandie' battled long over the North Atlantic speed record. Sometimes the one ship was a tenth of a knot faster than the other, but after a while the 'Queen Mary' became the victor in the prestige struggle. The 'Normandie' certainly had a somewhat better steam consumption than the 'Queen Mary', but on the other hand greater transmission losses from the turbines to the propellers through the electric drive. Furthermore, the 'Normandie' had definitely better lines, and thus less drag resistance. But the 63 rev/min lower propeller speed of the 'Queen Mary' gave her a 5 to 7 per cent gain over the

'Normandie'. Probably, it was the larger and slower propellers that gave the 'Queen Mary' that extra tenth of a knot needed to win the Blue Riband.

Like her sister ship, 'Queen Elizabeth', the 'Queen Mary' served as a troopship through-out the war. Both vessels were returned to the North Atlantic passenger route for a while after the war. But during the fifties it became more and more obvious that the airlines were taking a larger share of the passenger traffic across the Atlantic. In 1965, both ships were considered to have done their duty, and both were sold. The 'Queen Mary' became an hotel and exhibition vessel at Long Beach in California, where she still lies tied up at the quayside to the great enjoyment of many visitors.

The 'Queen Elizabeth' entered service four years later than her sister, but was built to much the same design, although slightly larger, and had somewhat higher steam data. The 'Queen Elizabeth' met a tragic end, when she was to be taken over by her new Hong Kong owner, who intended using her as an hotel and school ship. Fire broke out, and the vessel remained a wreck for a long while off Hong Kong before she was scrapped in 1972.

7.6 United States

Because of unparalleled progress in her standard of living, the United States found it dif-ficult to compete upon the high seas. Building costs in American yards during the fifties were more than double those in European yards. Crew costs were also double the European, and even more compared with those of the Greeks, Japanese and other industrialized na-tions. Almost all passenger traffic under the American flag, therefore, had to be subsidized by the Government. American merchant ships sailed mainly under Panamanian or Liberian flags. During the First World War, however, the 'Leviathan' had shown the vital importance of the large passenger liners for troop transportation during political crises. The 'Queen Mary' and 'Queen Elizabeth' had demonstrated their enormous transport capacity during the Second World War.

After the Second World War, and when the Cold War had brought back political tensions in the world, Congress decided that the United States also should acquire a large, fast pas-senger liner. The designing was entrusted to William Gibbs of the consulting firm, Gibbs and Cox. The order was placed with the well-known yard of Newport News on the east coast.

The ship was smaller than the previous giants, being about the same size as the 'Bremen' and 'Europa', with a tonnage of 53 300 BRT, fig. 121. Gibbs gave her unusually slender lines, and an energy-saving bulb. Although the displacement was less, her length was only 10 metres short of the 'Queen' ships. Gibbs installed a normal warship machinery on four shafts, built to give a continuous output of $4 \times 45\,000$ kW (240 000 shp). Her power was thus 3.4 kW/BRT compared with 1.5 kW/BRT for the 'Queens' — more than double the power per ton!

In spite of the high power, the weight of the machinery was considerably lower than for the 'Queens'. The specific steam consumption was also markedly less, partly because of the higher steam conditions, 61 bar, 540°C (870 lb/in^2, 1 000°F), and partly because the Westinghouse high speed impulse turbines were far better designed. The design of the ma-chinery was a classified secret for a long time, but after some years it has been possible to get some information. The ship, fig. 121, gave an enormous impression of power and speed with her two very large funnels. By designing the twelve water tube boilers for advanced steam conditions, 61 bar, 540°C, high forced draught pressure and furnace loadings, the boiler manufacturers managed to make the boilers so compact that William Gibbs could

Fig. 121. 'United States' from 1952. 53 000 BRT, 35.5 knots, 180 000 kW (240 000 shp).

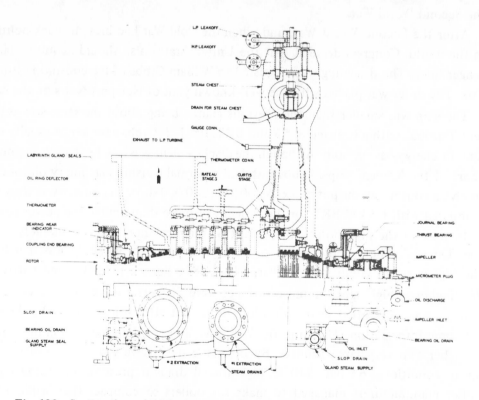

Fig. 122. Section through high pressure turbine for the 'United States'.
61 bar, 540°C (885 lb/in², 1 004°F), 4 750 rev/min.

Fig. 123. Photo of 'United States' low pressure turbine.

arrange them in only two boiler rooms. The boilers had economisers and air preheaters, and thus high efficiencies.

The turbine units were very simple, and consisted of four double reduction, cross-compound machines, designed on similar lines to the units developed for the large aircraft carriers. Special importance, however, had been given to the steam economy. Turbine speeds were high, almost 5 000 rev/min for the high pressure turbines, and slightly over 4 000 rev/min for the low pressure turbines at full power. The high pressure turbine, fig. 122, had only one Curtis wheel and six impulse wheels. It is perhaps surprising that the designers chose a Curtis wheel with an efficiency somewhat lower, for example, than if nine impulse wheels had been chosen. Land-based designs were used for the single-seated governing valves, actuated by an internal lever, small valve plugs and Venturi nozzles leading to the nozzle groups. The low pressure turbine, fig. 123, was of the usual American warship type with two parallel Curtis wheels followed by impulse wheels for astern operation. The speed was high — over 4 000 rev/min.

The propeller speed could be kept low — 188 rev/min — despite the high turbine speeds by using double reduction gearing. The gearing was the usual locked-train design of the same type developed for the aircraft carriers. The teeth were hobbed, shaved and shot-peened, enabling tooth loadings of 10-12.5 bar (150-180 lb/in^2) to be used. Small module teeth were used to get the quietest possible gears and with low vibration levels, as shown by fig. 124. The gearing was an all-welded design, and extremely light for its power, 45 000 kW (60 000 shp). The entire machinery was a pronounced warship design, exceedingly lightly built, using only forged, cast or sheet steel, and no components in cast or nodular iron. She had the speed of a cruiser. Normal speed was 34 knots, and more than 35.5 knots were obtained without overtaxing the machinery. The ship was considered capable of 40 knots at maximum speed.

Despite the very high machinery output and the high speed of the 'United States' compared with her predecessors, the oil consumption per passenger and crossing was no higher than for the 'Queens' — namely about 2.3 tons. This was achieved by better efficiencies, higher steam data, lower machinery weights and better hull lines. As long as oil prices were low and bookings were good, losses could be kept within reasonable limits.

But the increasingly dominant position of the airlines for carrying passengers across the Atlantic meant that bookings fell off and losses increased. In 1963, the ship was 'mothballed', and in 1973 she was taken over by the Maritime Administration in reserve as a troop transport ship.

As a feat of shipbuilding, the 'United States' is one of the foremost engineering achievements ever made, even though right from the outset she was an extraordinarily uneconomic effort, aimed primarily at prestige.

Fig. 124. Photo of 'United States' double reduction, locked-train gearing.
Speed, 4 750/4 005/188 rev/min. Power, 45 000 kW (60 000 shp).

7.7 France

After the loss of the 'Normandie', the French shipping lines kept their North Atlantic traffic going with slower ships of less distinction. In 1959, however, it was decided that once again the capabilities of French shipbuilders would be demonstrated with a large passenger ship. She was named 'France', and began operation in 1962. The ship was designed with very sharp lines, and broke at least one record — she was a few tenths of a metre longer than the 'Queen Elizabeth', the previous record holder for length. On the other hand, the owners did not try for any prestige speed, but specified a service speed of 31 knots. Architecturally, the ship was extremely beautiful. The characteristic wings on the funnels were to prevent the smoke from billowing down along the funnel sides. She was larger than the 'United States', but considerably smaller than the 'Normandie', fig. 125. Tonnage was 66 300 BRT. With a power of 4×30 000 kW (160 000 shp), she had a normal speed of 31 knots, and a maximum speed of 33 knots.

Fig. 125. 'France' of 1962. 66 300 BRT, 33 knots, 120 000 kW (160 000 shp).

Steam conditions were somewhat more conservative than for the 'United States', but probably represented the optimum in regard to steam consumption and reliability with 72 bar (1 030 lb/in²) and 500°C (932°F). She was built at Chantiers de l'Atlantique at Saint-Nazaire. The turbo-machinery was built by Companie Electromécanique in Paris, a subsidiary of Brown Boveri. The machinery arrangement is shown by fig. 126. The turbine designers chose single reduction gearing, and thus were forced to use four turbine cylinders. Propeller speed was extremely low, 156 rev/min, which ensured an extremely good propeller efficiency. To keep the dimensions of the turbines at a reasonable level, the gearing was made with the extraordinarily high reduction ratio of 19/1 for the high pressure pinion. The four turbine rotors had all low speeds, the high pressure turbine running at 3 044 rev/min, and the low pressure turbine at 2224 rev/min, fig. 128. The machinery thus consisted of one high pressure, two intermediate pressure and one low pressure turbines, all of Brown Boveri reaction type, fig. 127. The second intermediate and low pressure turbines were placed so high that the condenser could be put under the low pressure turbine, which gave a tidier arrangement than on the 'Queens'. The arrangement of the machinery and gearing is shown by figs 127 and 129.

The machinery was automated to a considerable degree, so that the engine room staff could be reduced to a minimum. The ship's machinery proved to be very reliable, and no

149

reports of breakdowns exist. Competition from the airlines combined with rising price of oil, however, made the ship quite uneconomic, and for the past few years she has been used for cruising under Norwegian management. Her power has been reduced to about a quarter, and her speed will stay around twenty-two knots. In her day, 'France' was considered to be the best appointed, most comfortable and smoothest-running ship on the North Atlantic.

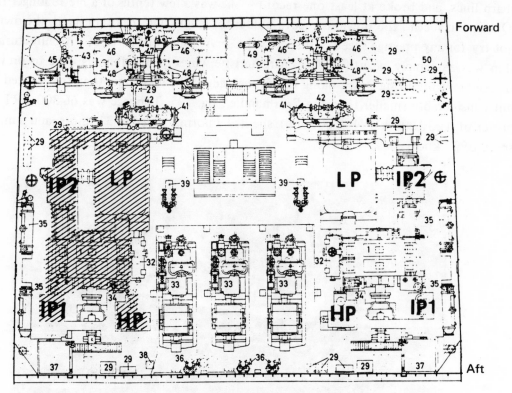

Fig. 126. Forward turbine arrangement on the 'France', with the main turbines on the outboard shafts and three turbo-generators.

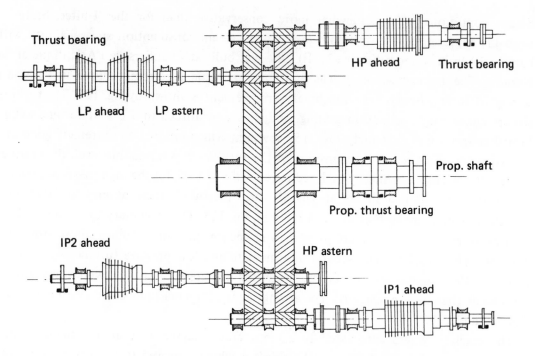

Fig. 127. Turbine arrangement on the 'France'.

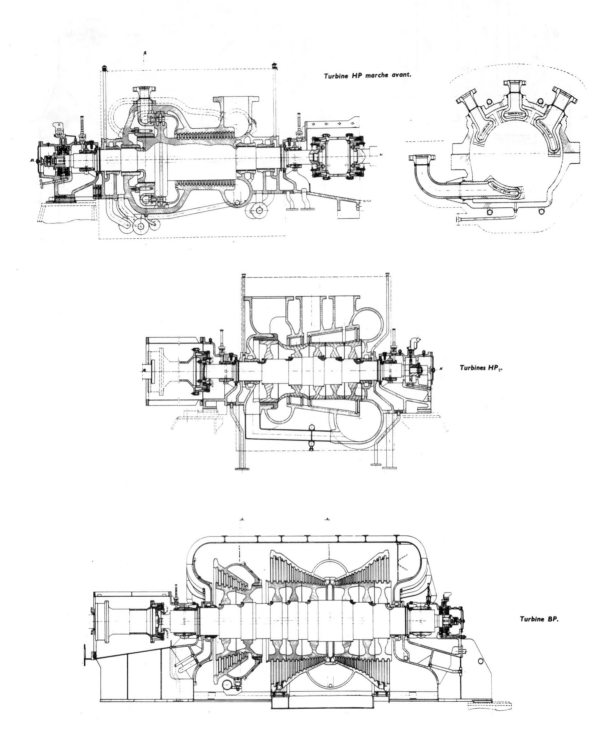

Turbine HP marche avant.

Turbines HP₂.

Turbine BP.

Fig. 128. Turbines on the 'France'.

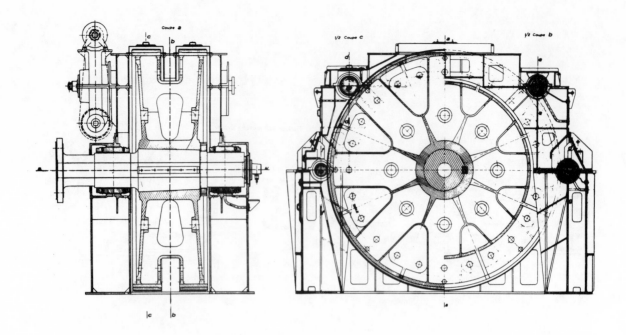

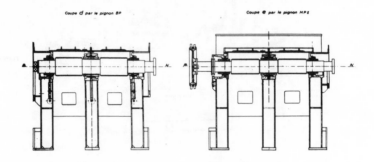

Fig. 129. Reduction gear on the 'France'.

Fig. 130. 'Queen Elizabeth 2' from 1969.

7.8 Queen Elizabeth 2

Some years after the 'Queen Mary' and the 'Queen Elizabeth' began to show signs of age and poor economy, a discussion began within the Cunard Line whether to accept that the airlines would take over the entire Atlantic traffic, or whether to make one more attempt to keep ocean traffic alive with a new, comfortable and relatively economic passenger liner. The project was christened 'Q4', and a lot of variations in the size and design of the new ship were discussed in the technical press. Thirty years had passed since the 'Queen Elizabeth' had been a project, and at full power she could produce 135 000 kW (181 700 shp). But now the Blue Riband was not an objective. A solution was sought whereby the ship could sail as a cruising liner during the winter season, should trans-Atlantic passengers want to go by air during that part of the year. The ship, however, did grow to be quite large for a cruising liner, about the same size as the 'France', with a tonnage of 65 862 BRT.

On the other hand, her service speed was reduced to 28 knots, with 29 1/2 knots as a maximum. The power could then be reduced so far that only two propellers were required. The power thus became 2×41 000 kW (110 000 shp). By using the thirty years of experience gained in boiler design and construction, the number of boilers could be reduced to three, whereby the ship got her distinctive profile, fig. 130, with only one funnel.

In this case, too, Cunard chose to order the ship from John Brown. The turbines were manufactured in their engine shops. But the design was done by Pametrada, the communal design and development company for builders of Parsons machinery. Pametrada followed to a certain extent the design principles successfully developed by the impulse manufacturers.

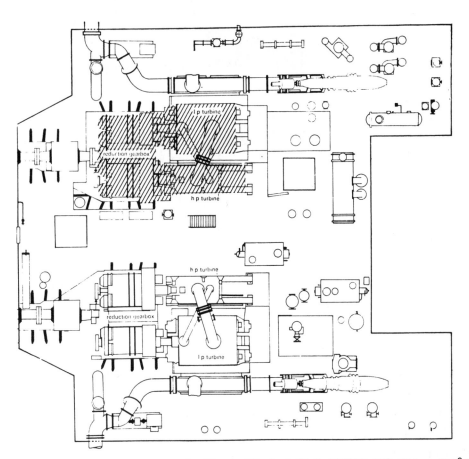

Fig. 131. Machinery arrangement for 'Queen Elizabeth 2'. 2×GG(HP+LP), 60 bar, 510°C (870 lb/in², 950°F). 2×41 000 kW (110 000 shp) 5 207/3 192/174 rev/min.

The machinery arrangement consisted, therefore, of two double reduction, cross-compound units, shown in fig. 131. The arrangement was relatively simple. Pametrada's decision (at the owners' request) to use two astern turbines connected in series, one on the HP pinion and one on the LP pinion, complicated the arrangement, however, when compared with that of the 'United States'.

A relatively low steam pressure, but an international standard superheat at 60 bar, 510°C (855 lb/in², 950°F) was chosen for the three boilers. In spite of the double reduction gearing the propeller speed was chosen as 174 rev/min, probably the optimum for machinery with only two propellers and the record-high power of 41 000 kW (55 000 shp) per propeller.

The high pressure turbines, fig. 132, had one Curtis wheel and eleven impulse stages, and a speed of 5 207 rev/min at full speed. Pametrada decided to build the HP turbine with a double casing and welded-in nozzle chambers. The high pressure astern turbine, a single Curtis wheel, was coupled to the forward end of the ahead turbine. From a purely manoeuvring aspect, this turbine was unnecessary, as sufficient astern power could be obtained with a single Curtis plus a single wheel in the low pressure turbine. But, to satisfy the owners, Pametrada accepted the complication in the interest of increased safety.

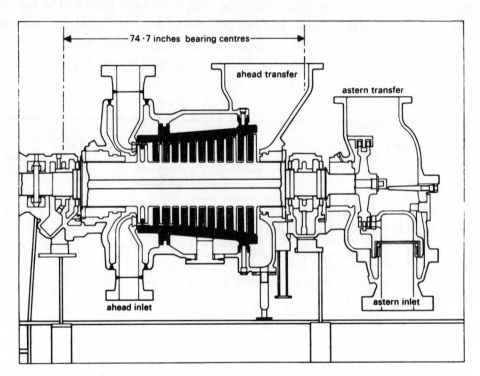

Fig. 132. Section through HP turbine for 'Queen Elizabeth 2', with a separate HP astern casing. Designed by Pametrada.

The low pressure turbine of Pametrada design had machined discs and double flow, fig. 133. A low pressure astern turbine, consisting of two single wheels, was built into the aft end of the low pressure rotor.

During her trials, 'Queen Elizabeth 2' suffered a number of mishaps to her machinery that were much discussed in the press, as well as in Parliament. Several rows of moving blades in the HP turbines failed. The subsequent Parliamentary investigating commission found that the blades had been designed without account being taken of the risks of blade vibration in

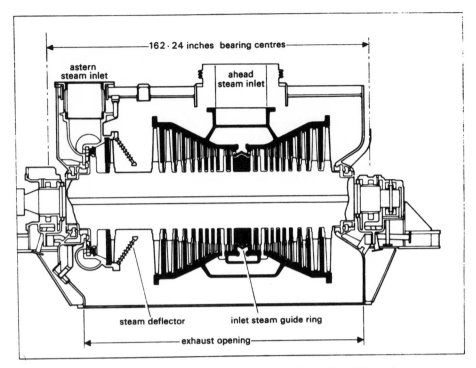

Fig. 133. Low pressure turbine for 'Queen Elizabeth 2'. 3 192 rev/min.

resonance with the vortices from the stationary guide vanes. This classic error, which General Electric of U.S.A. suffered painfully for during the twenties and de Stal Laval in the forties, and which put paid to the Brown-Curtis turbines in Britain during the twenties and thirties, had apparently been forgotten by Pametrada. After reblading the HP turbines, the ship has since been operational, but she has been subjected to a number of other types of breakdown which initially gave her a dubios reputation. During 1983, however, the 'Queen Elizabeth 2' was still carrying passengers across the North Atlantic during the summer season, and seems to have been relatively well booked-up. At other times of the year, this large ship, with accommodation for 2 000 passengers, is used as a cruising liner. With the oil prices of the late seventies and early eighties, the machinery power and the speed are almost certainly economically excessive. The question is whether also this machinery, like that of nearly all the fast supertankers and container ships, must be rebuilt to operate at lower and more economic speeds, or even converted to diesel or diesel-electric drive.

From the 'Mauretania' and 'Lusitania' to the 'Queen Elizabeth 2' covered a period from 1907 to 1980. Ships grew in size and speeds increased by stages up until the Second World War, culminating with the 'United States' and her 240 000 shp and 35 knots at the end of the epoch. Since then, development has stagnated. Now, the time of the large turbine ships seems definitely past. Large passenger ships will continue to be built, but it is hardly likely that they will be turbine-driven. It is improbable that such ships will be built with greater powers than 50 000 kW (70 000 shp). The era of the great steam turbine-driven passenger ships lasted more than 70 years.

8. ENGINE ROOM MEMORIES

My first tour of duty with the Swedish Navy was during the summers of 1927 and 1928, when I received instruction as a naval engineer trainee on the iron-clad 'Drottning Victoria'. The Westinghouse turbines on the ship ran like sewing machines, but coal-firing and the 12 Yarrow boilers meant hard and dirty slave labour. Bunkering was done at least once a month. The entire crew, seamen and cadets, as well as some of the officers, functioned as loading devices. Each was given a basket, and we ran like coolies, carrying baskets of coal upon our backs. It was not long before the inexperienced got sores on their backs. But after a while one learned how to tie an old sweater to make a cushion that the coal basket could rest upon. Bunkering usually started about 6 or 7 o'clock in the morning, and if the coal dump was a long distance from the ship, we seldom finished running backwards and forwards with our baskets until late in the evening. Usually between 3–500 tons had to be taken aboard using only manual labour.

After a few hours, everyone was as black as negroes. To keep the accommodation as clean as possible, they were placed 'out of bounds' to us coolies. There was only one feeding place — we ate standing at a long table placed on the quay. To prevent us getting sick by drinking too much liquid during warm weather, fruit drinks were mixed with oatmeal. This was an old remedy for stopping stomach cramps.

When bunkering was concluded, it took a whole day's cleaning up to get the ship reasonably free from coal dust, despite all the efforts made to keep it out. To lie in a bunker with only a few decimetres between the coal and the deck–head with a continual steam of coal flowing down from the heap on deck, and trimming the black mixture of large lumps of coal and dust up against the deck and deck-beams in almost pitch darkness, was hardly healthy work. Coal-heaving from the bunkers to the boilers was done manually, as was also stoking the fuel into the furnaces.

Only ash-disposal was not done manually, and then only at sea. Ash was ejected overboard when the ship had cleared harbour, using water–jet ejectors. Firing was done by a stoker who shoveled the coal into the furnace, assisted by a trainee who opened and closed the furnace door. It was precision work to place the coal in the right place and of the right amount, so as to make an even layer on the grate with no holes that the forced draught could blow through. If a shovelfull of dust was thrown onto the wrong place, it would vanish up the smoke stacks without being burnt.

The hardest work in the stokehold, and the most trying, was when the coal fires were to be clinkered. The fire was banked so that the unburnt coal was pushed over to one side. The clinker was raked out from the uncovered side through openings, using long rakes. Slag deposits were chipped off with long iron bars. The glowing material fell onto the floor plates. Water was sprayed on it to cool the ashes quickly. The steam and gases produced by this would assuredly not be approved by the environmental experts of today, but sickness among the stokehold crew was rare.

On the other hand, it happened that the untrained sons of the gentry among the trainees and cadets collapsed. The general atmosphere in the stokehold was hardly drawingroom-like, but I never witnessed any cruelty, even if the work was hard and the discipline strict. On the contrary, with the stoker's permission, I was on several occasions allowed to take a nap in a bunker when I could manage no more. Stoking was definitely no sinecure, but the work had one thing going for it. The four hour watches vanished in a jiffy. Watches in the turbine and condenser rooms, however, often dragged on and were boring.

The engineering cadets had stokehold duty outside their lesson periods, which latter took up six hours each day. Training consisted of seamanship, artillery and torpedo handling. Technical training included making layout sketches of all the pipework, learning every nook and cranny onboard, and being able to draw a midship section with all the principal dimensions. Our worst duty was 24-hour watches in the diesel dynamo room with the ship hove-to. When you went up for a meal, you had to be relieved by a fellow-trainee.

The only duties in the dynamo room were to keep the lubricators full of oil, and check that the engines were behaving as they should. Every half hour, temperatures and pressures were recorded from several gauges. To keep awake during the dog and dawn watches was anything but easy, and often did not work. A good way was to sit with your head against a ladder from deck. When the engineer came for an occasional check, the ladder shook and woke the sleeper. Another way to keep awake was to sit on your stool with a large spanner held in both hands. If you dropped off to sleep, the spanner fell on the deck plates and made such a racket that the sleeper awoke.

Discipline was iron-hard, and spare time just did not exist. If it ever happened that you had some time to yourself, it was better to sleep and catch up with all the lost night hours. We lived 12 men in a tiny mess which was very tight for space. At night, hammocks were slung which could only be used between 2100 and 0600 hours. If you wanted to sleep at any other time, you had to stretch out on the mess floor, or on the narrow rock-hard benches that were our seating at the table.

The mess area was less than 2 m² per cadet. There we slept, ate, had our lessons and did our homework. The food had little of today's school lunch quality, but there was plenty of crisp-bread. Butter, however, was tightly rationed, and potatoes were often going rotten. An emergency measure for hunger was to go to the canteen and buy some buns. Fresh vegetables did not exist, but if we were in contact with land there was usually milk. We had an issue of beer each day like the rest of the crew. Many of us preferred to cash in our beer ration and use the money in the canteen. We suffered from an eternal lack of sleep, and could drop-off in any situation, even with open eyes during lessons.

A lasting memory is my first duty in a stokehold. Upon coming down, I was told to help by opening the furnace door, and got plenty of ribald advice on how to do it. The door must not be open a second too long and let cold air into the furnace. On the other hand, the door must not prevent a single lump of coal from entering the furnace, when the stoker threw in a shovelfull. During a pause in the work, a huge, kindly stoker threw his coal-shovel on a heap of coal and told me to sit on it and take a rest. When I sat down, the shovel was burning hot having been placed in the furnace to heat up. This idea was obviously to see how chicken-hearted the little cadet was. Not to endure this trial by fire would have meant some tough days ahead in the stokehold. Luckily, despite my burning rump, I managed to smile and thank him for the 'warm-hearted reception'. After that, I was accepted as one of the stokehold crew and had no serious trouble during our time together.

In spite of the coal that got everywhere, this period in the Navy was one of tidiness and cleanliness. Every brass fitting was polished and shining, and everything was looked after with motherly care. Once a week came inspection, and God help those who did not have their section clean and tidy. We laundered our own working clothes, washing them with lye in a stokehold bucket which was 'steamed' using a steam hose. The treatment was very effective, but not very easy on the material. During the daytime, we had to wear white shirts, although we often had watchkeeping in the stokehold, combined with instruction. Keeping our shirts something like white, therefore, posed a difficult problem. We soon learnt to wear 'the white shirt' for Monday morning parades and inspections. As soon as inspection was over, before lessons began, we ran below to change the white shirt for an older and dirtier one.

After two summers on the ironclad, I had a summer's practical training in the Karlskrona naval yard, followed by a summer at Brown Boveri's works in Switzerland. During the summer of 1931, I was second engineer on the old coal-fired destroyer 'Hugin', the first Swedish destroyer with direct-drive turbines. She was a terrible consumer of coal. The months on board that ship seem to have consisted solely of bunkering and coal-heaving. She was kept very clean, however, which did not prevent the coal dust from impregnating the skin, so that even fourteen days after going ashore you would still be sweating black. After serving on the 'Hugin'. I was transferred to the almost brand-new destroyer, 'Ehrensköld', the pride of the Fleet. 'Ehrensköld' was oil-fired and was as clean as a sick bay. No coal dust, and the brass-work was gleaming and polished. All the paintwork was spotless. In spite of this, the stokers posted from the 'Hugin' did not like it. There was nothing to do during watchkeeping. Only look after a lot of pressure gauges and level glasses, so the watches seemed endlessly long. Some of the stokers requested a posting back to the 'Hugin'. They could not stand the long watches with oil-fired boilers. They yearned back to coal-firing and hard physical labour.

In the autumn of 1933, I came home from a training period in England to partake in the trials of the aircraft-carrying cruiser 'Gotland'. Hugo Hammar, director of Götaverken, gave me a warm welcome, and I was able to help out with various problems. It had been a while since Götaverken had built a large warship, and a lot of things did not work out properly. When the lifeboats were to be hauled aboard, for example, the davits collapsed as the deck that supported them was too weak for the heavy weight. During the week before the yard trials, the ship seemed like an ant hill. Organization and planning left much to be desired, especially as there was no clear-cut division of responsibility between the shipyard and the Naval Administration. This caused a lot of trouble. Naval Administration supplied the aircraft catapult, and from the beginning this did not seem to work at all. Launch after launch was made with dummy weights representing the airplane, but neither acceleration nor firing speed was sufficient. Despite the disorder, the ship sailed on her yard trials.

I served as recorder in one of the boiler rooms, and had to fill in figures on a report sheet every ten minutes. When we cleared Vinga lighthouse off Gothenburg, speed was increased, and burner after burner was lit in the boilers. To judge from the vibrations, we had come up to a pretty good speed. Then, without any warning, a serious accident occurred, about which a lot was written in the newspapers.

Down in the stokehold, we heard a series of terrible bangs in the steam piping. The fans squealed like pigs, and the speed sank rapidly. Then pitch darkness as the electricity failed. The watch engineer did the right thing, he tripped the boilers. It was as black as the grave, and steam hissed out from many places. We fumbled after the emergency lighting that we knew should be somewhere. When we did find the switch no light came! We stood there like idiots in the darkness, listening to one violent crash after another from water-hammer in the steam pipes. Steam hissed, and we expected the steam pipes to burst. In a while, we got up on deck. After an eternity, the diesel generators started and the lights came on.

This was what had happened. At low speeds, the boilers were normally supplied by steam-driven reciprocating feed pumps. At higher boiler loadings, the turbine-driven feed pumps were to be connected in. An artificer had started his turbo-feed pump in good time during the speed-up ready for connecting to the feed water lines. The control valve to the boiler was, however, wide open. During reciprocating feed pump operation, the flow is regulated by setting the pump steam valve to suit the demand for feed water. The feed valve was therefore fully open. When the turbo-feed pumps operate, the feed water levels and flows are controlled by throttling the feed valve. When the operator started the turbo-feed pump, therefore, its entire delivery was pumped without throttling into the boiler. This filled up to the top, and water mixed with steam primed into both main and auxiliary piping. The consequence was violent water hammer and a lot of the auxiliary machinery tripped out. The turbo-generators got water instead of steam and slowed down. The generators were consequently tripped from the network, resulting in a blackout for the entire ship.

Most serious of all, however, was that the steering gear ceased to function. Thus the rudder did not move when the wheel was turned on the bridge. Just at that moment, the ship was about to yaw to avoid a couple of fishing trawlers. At high speed, the 'Gotland' cut right through a fishing boat, with the consequence that two men were thrown into the sea and drowned. The entire incident was an experience that has engraved itself upon my memory.

It is not hard to understand that, thereafter, for all future trials, I made sure that the fitters got written orders for all rudder connections, and that these were properly checked at the quayside before the trials commenced. In the same way, before every day during the trials, we checked that the engine telegraphs worked, and tested the emergency lighting system by switching it on. Another lesson was that running things in partnership without a clear-cut division of responsibility between supplier and customer is asking for trouble. The 'Gotland', however, later completed her trials without greater difficulty.

In 1934, I was promoted to the duty of divisional engineer for destroyers 'Ehrensköld' and 'Nordenskjöld'. During a voyage in the 'Ehrensköld' from Karlskrona to Stockholm, I got a useful lesson. Due to careless navigation, 'Ehrensköld' went aground in poor visibility on the archipelago off the Östergötland coast, and tore a large hole in her bottom near the bows. By flooding a number of compartments aft, and going hard astern, the destroyer came free. We could, by and large, cope with the water leaking in forward, but we were fairly low in the water when we made the naval yard at Stockholm with all pumps running. The chief engineer in charge was contacted with a request for immediate docking as there was a risk that the bulkhead against the flooded compartments would collapse under the weight of water. This officer refused to do any work at all until he had received a working order from the yard commander back at Karlskrona.

By then, it was fairly late, and it would obviously take a long while to obtain a formal working order without preceding reports and the rest of the bureaucratic trappings. The destroyer, therefore, had to lay-to with her bilge pumps going flat out until this work order at long last floated in. When I showed my pent-up anger over this ridiculous bureaucracy, the engineer in charge — a wise old man — said to me:

> "Young man, one can exceed one's authority and do the right thing in a difficult situation, but then one gets into trouble for it, and the stupid bureaucratic regulations remain unchanged. If, however, I push regulations into absurdity and demonstrate their insanity by a painful example, perhaps after a while I can bring about an alteration in the regulations".

In the autumn of 1934, I served on the destroyer 'Klas Uggla'. The squadron included the 'Ehrensköld' and 'Nordenskjöld' as well. One bleak day in December the destroyers, much delayed after torpedo practice, were to tie-up at Helsingborg for the weekend and some shore leave. It was foggy, but because we were late, the squadron commander made 20 knots despite approaching the narrow end of Öresund with all its traffic. I was up on the bridge and found it rather scary to rush ahead at such a speed with no more visibility than about 50 metres. 'Ehrensköld' and 'Nordenskjöld' followed on-station on the starboard quarter, just visible through the fog.

Suddenly, with a terrible, loud noise, and a violent, drawn-out shock, the destroyer went right up on a shoal off the island of Ven. 'Ehrensköld' and 'Nordenskjöld' escaped by rapid manoeuvres. 'Klas Uggla's' bows were lifted up and the propellers stopped dead. Water rushed in forward in all the watertight compartments. Stokehold No. 1 quickly filled with water and we did not even manage to start the pumps. No. 2 stokehold could be kept for a while with the water level just over the deck plates by running the bilge pumps flat out. The leaks, however, increased as the ship settled on the shoal. The water surface rose, and the pumps could soon no longer be used when the level became too high.

The boiler in Stokehold No. 3 was the only one still with fire on. Water was coming in, but not to the same extent as in the forward boiler rooms. An uneven struggle between the pumps and the water streaming in continued for about two hours. Increasing leakage through the bottom plates, however, gave the water surely and mercilessly the upper hand. Soon the water ran into the fired boiler, which was under full pressure. The boiler had to be blown down, and then the whole stokehold was under water. For more than two weeks, the destroyer lay there in the cold, storm and fog, until the salvage ship, 'Fritiof', could get her off the shoal with two large pontoons.

They were exciting and instructive days for a young engineer. Salvage folk were a type of seaman that hardly exists today. They were experts at diving and seamanship, and could handle cables and heavy weights in an exceptional way. They could work around the clock without visible distress. I shall never forget the skipper of the 'Fritiof', Captain Hedberg, and all his salvage stories which he told during the night watches. At long last, with a pontoon on either side to stabilize and support her, the 'Klas Uggla' was ignominiously towed to Kockums yard to have almost the whole of her bottom renewed. All hull plates were riveted in those days, which made such a repair very much easier. The destroyer was supported on timber props while her bottom was replated. There was much to learn here too for a young engineer. The captain had to remain aboard during the entire repair, a very light punishment compared with the one awaiting him after the court martial. He ordered, however, his squadron engineer to keep him company. That sojourn aboard the destroyer in an icy, damp and windy Malmö, with a few electric stoves in the cabins, which had no internal insulation against the winter cold, was not particularly pleasant. The captain's despair, and the resigned atmosphere at mealtimes in the wardroom remain a haunting memory.

After the 'Klas Uggla' was repaired, I was given the job of organizing a series of trials to verify that the machinery was in good order, despite bent and straightened shafts, and despite the hardships endured by the aft boiler. During the trials, the official speed of 36 knots could not be attained. Full power gave only 34 knots, although the destroyer had a clean bottom. The main reason for this worsening of performance was that the design displacement of 1 000 tons was a theoretical and unrealistic figure. The actual figure, fully bunkered, was about 1 200 tons, or 20 per cent greater. As a general rule, the power requirement for a given speed is reckoned to vary linearly with the displacement. This meant a speed reduction by abour 1 1/2 knots with the larger displacement. An extra 1/2 knot was due to deterioration of the turbine blade finish, and deposits in the condenser tubing which gave a poorer vacuum. For the Naval Administration, the report on the impaired speed characteristic of the destroyer came as a surprise.

By the summer of 1936, the destroyer 'Göteborg' was ready, and I was ordered to take charge of her engine trials. These provided a couple of months with many interesting experiences. The destroyer was the Navy's first ship fitted with scoops for supplying cooling water to the condensers. The powerful, turbine-driven cooling water pumps were automatically started for stop and slow steaming ahead or astern.

The commanding officer was one of the Navy's best destroyer captains, with a reputation for stylish and successful manoeuvring. Although the yard offered help, he decided to take the ship through the narrow Götaverken channel and into the river under her own steam. The destroyer was moored to one of the floating docks. It was a beautiful summer day, and the deck was crowded with spectators made up from the crew and a large contingent of engineers and workers from the shipyard. All were looking forward to an interesting day of trials. The ship's chief engineer was in his usual place in the starboard turbine room. We were all, of course, excited about how the new and untried machinery would behave.

First the telegraph rang down 'Astern, dead slow on both engines'. Nothing happened. After that, the bridge rang down 'Astern, slow on both engines' – nothing happened! There was a pause for a while, then the order was rung 'Astern, half speed on both engines'. That brought the ship to life, and with a jerk she leaped rapidly backwards. Startled, the captain rang stop on both engines. Then, to everybody's surprise, the destroyer went forward at a tidy speed and rammed the dock with her bows so that the timbers splintered.

There was a pause, and then the telegraph rang again 'Astern, dead slow', but the destroyer still lay with her bows against the wooden dock. Then came 'Astern, slow', and finally 'Astern, half speed' and the whole procedure was repeated with a violent jump astern followed by 'Stop'. Once again the destroyer took a run forward and slammed into the already damaged dockside. The chain of events now became clear to me.

The turbine operators had had a bit of trouble with the vacuum during standstill, and as a consequence had speeded up the cooling water pumps to the maximum. The jets of cooling water coming out of the scoops gave a powerful reaction force driving the ship. Not until the astern manoeuvre was strong enough to counteract this ahead force did the destroyer move astern. After the chief realized what was happening and throttled back the cooling water pumps, we managed to get out into the river. During trials at sea, it was found that the destroyer could make between 6 and 7 knots ahead just with the cooling water pumps going flat out.

Everybody was very impressed at the sight of the destroyer cutting through the water like a knife at 40 knots. The astern trials were a real experience. She stopped from full speed to dead in the water within just over a ship's length, and it took just under a minute. The whole sea boiled when the astern manoeuvre came. The stern shook violently, and loud bangs were heard when the propellers cavitated.

After the trials on the 'Göteborg', I moved abroad and worked at Brown Boveri. War was approaching, however, and in 1939 I was recalled to run the trials on the destroyer 'Malmö' at Eriksbergs yard. She was sister ship to the 'Göteborg', and the trials went off without any difficulties or sensations.

Naval mobilization in 1939 was one great chaos. The Swedish authorities could definitely not be awarded any prizes for their organizing capabilities before mobilization. Indeed, several crews were mustered for cruisers and ships that had already been scrapped. Auxiliary vessels that had been scrapped were recalled for service. I was ordered to deal with a large tug from Norrland. The reason why she had not reported to the Kalmar dockyard on the East Coast was that there was no navigable passage from Storsjön, one of Sweden's large inland lakes! This apparently had not bothered the people who had worked out the mobilization plants.

In 1940, I was posted to Gothenburg as project leader for rebuilding the machinery on the 'Ehrensköld' and 'Nordenskjöld' at the Götaverken yard. The destroyers were to get new Penhoêt boilers. In April, during the invasion of Denmark and Norway, the first spin tests on the 'Ehrensköld' were ready to commence. We found that we could not get any draught pressure in the stokehold. In spite of the turbo-fans going at full speed, we could get no more than a few centimetres of air pressure. When we went out for sea trials, the fans were running at full speed, but the destroyer made no more than 18 knots.

A painter with his paint pot down in the stokehold solved the problem. He found that he could paint the fan housing without the paint blowing away, which had not been possible on the previous destroyer. Destroyers at that time had sealed stokeholds, which meant that they were under full air pressure, the fans discharging directly into the boiler room. When the fans were slowed down, we found that the painter was right. The fan impeller, to everyone's surprise, went in the wrong direction! A telephone call to the chief designer at de Laval, clarified the situation, although he too could hardly believe his ears at first.

It turned out that when the fans were rebuilt, de Laval's had provided them with new impellers. These were to give the new boilers a greater air supply, and a higher draught pressure. The impellers had been made from drawings for the 'Göteborg', but no one had noticed that those fan turbines had a different rotation. In the turmoil of mobilization, the fans were sent back to de Laval's at Nacka. The turbines were rebladed for the opposite rotation. Each night, two of the units were sent to Stockholm, and each morning two refurbished fans arrived at the yard and were installed. I still admire the achievement of the de Laval fitters and Götaverken's folk who managed to change out six turbo-fans and reblade them in somewhat less than a week.

When the fans were reinstalled, the trials could be resumed. But then another still not fully explained breakdown occurred. Steam leakage to the funnels was reported already at about half power, first in one boiler and then in another. When the tubes were inspected at the yard, the ones nearest the burners had considerable bulges in them. The tubes had obviously overheated locally, so that the material became incandescent and swelled up. A couple of the bulges had burst, which was the reason for the report of steam leakage.

The three boilers were inspected, and the same damages were found in all of them. It was not to be wondered that a great commotion broke out among the Naval Administration as well as at the yard and on board the ship. Boiler experts scurried to the ship, and all tried to find fault with the operation or the tube material, but without result. Time after time the operators were made to tell what had happened. It all seemed inexplicable. The two inner tube rows were retubed in record time. Work went amazingly quickly, and at the next trial run the destroyer was well supplied with boiler experts, both real and self-appointed.

The boiler trial began with only one boiler as a precautionary measure. Already at 3/4 load, the tubes nearest the furnace began to have glowing bulges. In spite of all the expert advice, the destroyer had to return with yet another set of failed tubes. Most of the tubes in the two inner rows had to be renewed. The only probability for the cause of failure proved later to be the fuel oil used. This was an extremely light Aruba oil of diesel type. Tests showed that this oil could give an extremely intense blue flame when burned. Insufficient circulation in the inner tube rows, and high surface loading in the flame area, had apparently given such high local temperatures that the tubes had become completely full of steam and thus overheated. Because of this breakdown, the Navy's vessels were banned from using such light fraction oils. In this way, the fierce flames that had been observed could be avoided. An absolutely clear-cut account of the matter was never obtained, but after changing the boiler fuel, the trials went off all right.

In 1941, I was detailed to assist with the design of four coastal destroyers. When the New-building Centre was formed at Gothenburg to lead naval construction at the private yards, my task was the coordination of the machinery designs. The coastal destroyers were built under exceedingly urgent circumstances. Swedish industry badly needed work, and contributed wholeheartedly with rapid designs and short deliveries, bypassing the usual red tape.

No sooner had the Newbuilding Centre got the coastal destroyers on the slipways when the Hårsfjärd disaster occurred, with the loss of three 'City' class destroyers caused by a bomb placed in an ammunition in one of the destroyers magazine. Four modified 'City' class destroyers were built as replacement under the hectic wartime conditions. The ships of both series were extremely interesting jobs, but the machinery was largely based on well-proven designs with little new development or ideas.

I was rather happy when ordered to assist with the machinery for the cruiser project 'Tre Kronor' during 1942–1943. Based to some extent upon an Italian proposal, new specifications were produced in line with what Swedish industry could accomplish. In 1944 I was employed by Götaverken primarily to look after the building of the cruisers, and was directly responsible to the technical director. Götaverken had by then an extraordinarily experienced staff for warship construction, and despite difficulty in obtaining materials, the building advanced rapidly. The work on the 'Tre Kronor' and 'Göta Lejon' gave valuable experience, a lot of work and very little free time.

The full speed trial was not entirely successful. Initially, everything went well when the speed was increased. The boilers were loaded separately, one by one, up to full power, and behaved according to calculation. At higher speeds, however, considerable vibrations appeared at the stern, excited by the propellers. The propeller shafts were supported in oil-lubricated babbit bearings, and were sealed from ingress of sea water by spring-loaded seals of the Cedervall type. At speeds in excess of 25 knots, the oil pressure in the propeller bearings disappeared, and the oil leaked out. Steam and salt water came out of the test cocks instead of oil. The propeller shafts obviously vibrated and apparently with an axial movement of such magnitude that the flat radial sealing faces could not keep tight.

At 28 knots, the bearing sleeves ran more with sea water than oil as lubricating medium. After consulting with the foreman responsible, I reported a serious risk of the propeller bearings seizing. Ignominiously, we returned to the yard without having achieved more than 28–29 knots. The problem was got over, however, by replacing the propeller bearings by water-lubricated bearings of lignum vitae, a conventional design used since the 1800's, and regarded as reliable, even under heavy vibrations from the propellers. After comprehensive tests on the propellers in the cavitation tank at Karlstad, the design of the shaft support was changed. It had previously given a certain counter rotation of the water flow ahead of the propeller. This vortex movement had increased the propeller efficiency somewhat, but at the same time had obviously caused a serious cavitation problem. By these actions, the cavitation problem largely disappeared, and the propeller vibrations were reduced to an acceptable and harmless level, and the lignum vitae bearings gave no trouble.

I am very thankful for my years of service in the Navy. Great responsibilities were given to me early. I learned to respond and adapt to older men of great skill and experience, and found out how important discipline and team work is when ships are built and new designs are introduced and tested.